ENTERTAINMENT [illegible]OLOGY PRESS

In taking advantage of the latest in 'print on demand' digital printing techniques, Entertainment Technology Press is approaching book publishing in a very different way. By establishing a wide range of highly specific technical books that can be kept up-to-date in a continuing publishing process, our plan is to cover the entertainment technology sector with a wide range of individual titles.

As will be seen by examining the back cover of this book, the ETP list is divided into various categories so as to allow sufficient room for generic growth and development of each title. To ensure the quality of the books and the success of the project the publishers are building up a team of authors who are practising in and well-respected by the industry. As specialists within a particular field of activity it is anticipated that each author will stay closely involved with 'their' title or titles for an extended period.

All Entertainment Technology Press titles have a dedicated area on the publisher's own website at www.etnow.com where latest information and up-dates can be accessed by purchasers of the books concerned. This additional service is included within the purchase price of all titles.

Readers and prospective authors are invited to submit any ideas and comments they may have on the Entertainment Technology Press series to the Series Editor by email to editor@etnow.com.

Entertainment Technology Press Ltd
The Studio, High Green, Great Shelford, Cambridge CB2 5EG
Tel: +44 (0)1223 550805 Fax: +44 (0)1223 550806

FOCUS ON LIGHTING TECHNOLOGY

Richard Cadena

ENTERTAINMENT TECHNOLOGY PRESS

Systems Series

This book is dedicated to my supportive and loving wife, Lisa, and my beautiful daughter, Joey, who powers my dreams. Also, my mother, Yolanda, who taught me caring and compassion, and my father, Noe, the engineer and athlete who kindled those fires in me.

cover photo courtesy of High End Systems. Photo by Amy Davidson. Set and lighting design by Chas Herington. Equipment supplied by Zenith Lighting

FOCUS ON LIGHTING TECHNOLOGY

Richard Cadena

Entertainment Technology Press

Focus on Lighting Technology

This edition Published February 2002 by
Entertainment Technology Press Ltd
The Studio, High Green, Great Shelford, Cambridge, CB2 5EG
Internet: www.etnow.com

ISBN 1 904031 14 5

A title within the
Entertainment Technology Press Systems Series
Series editor: John Offord

FOLT / 001

CONTENTS

ACKNOWLEDGEMENTS

I've been told on more than one occasion that you can't expect to have a successful career in the entertainment lighting industry unless you spend some time living in one of the major entertainment centers – i.e. New York, Los Angeles, Orlando, or Las Vegas. On the contrary, I think it's more important who you spend time with, rather than where you spend your time. and to surround yourself with knowledgeable people. If that means having to relocate to the big city, then so be it. I've been fortunate enough to live in Austin, Texas for twenty-five years since I came here as a college freshman to study electrical engineering at the University of Texas. I've been lucky enough to be work with some of the most knowledgeable people and best companies in the industry, without whom this book would be the shortest in the world. I would like to acknowledge some of the people who helped me formulate the concepts and ideas for this book.

From the first day I met him, Richard Belliveau cast a big impression on me. Thanks for taking a chance on me and giving me my first job in the industry, and thanks for imparting your knowledge unselfishly. I should also mention Lowell Fowler and Bob Schacherl since we had a wonderful run for several years. I really enjoyed my time working and growing with you guys.

Thanks to Bruce Jordahl for giving me the opportunity to write for Pro Lights and Staging News magazine (www.plsn.com). If not for Bruce this project would never have taken seed. Thanks also to everyone at PLSN, and in particular publisher Terry Lowe for allowing me to contribute to the magazine. I must also thank John Offord, Ken Sewell, and Jackie Staines of Entertainment Technology Press, the publishers of this book.

I have many, many friends in the industry, too numerous to name. But I would be remiss if I didn't acknowledge the person who believed in me enough to take big chance at the time. Chas Herington has been a good friend and an inspiration since we met in 1989. When he brought us the Dire Straits *On Every Street* World Tour in 1991, it was a real door opener for my company and me and I'm forever grateful.

Thanks to all the lighting techs who I've had the opportunity to pick brains with – Don Pugh, Bill McCarty, Noel Duncan, Paul Pelltier, Lary Cotton, Woody Smith, Scott Ingham, Robby Bruce, Byron Ziegler, Rebecca Kitrell and lots, lots more. Thanks to the many PLSN readers who took the time and effort to write to me and ask me to publish a book of my work. This is for all of you – and most of all to Bob Gregory for giving me the idea. This book is his fault.

Thanks to my mother and father for giving me a proper upbringing and providing me the opportunity to go to college. Thanks to my daughter Joey for giving me extra inspiration to get out of bed every morning. Last but not least, I must acknowledge my wife, Lisa, for tolerating the long hours and total obsession with writing, re-writing, discussing, and generally annoying her with this book. I love you.

World Peace
Inner Harmony
Lasting Prosperity

Richard Cadena

1 ON YOUR MARKS, GET SET

"My interest is in the future because that's where I am going to live."

– Charles. F. Kettering, engineer and inventor of the electronic ignition for automobiles.

In a fitting start to the new millennium, the media blitz during the Y2K New Year's Eve celebrations prominently displayed the ubiquitous tools of our trade. Automated lighting was everywhere, splashed across the icons of the world: the Sydney Opera House, the Giza pyramids, Times Square, Manger Square in Bethlehem, and just about every other picture of the new millennium parties. You could hardly turn on the television or read a newspaper without seeing a free advertisement for one lighting company or another. The juxtaposition of the millennium event and automated lighting reminded me of two things: lighting technology has come a long way in the last century, and it is poised to make quantum leaps in the near future.

I recently saw a bumper sticker that said, "Get in. Sit down. Shut up. Hold on." That's the feeling I get about the future of automated lighting technology. Computers have helped us to do some wonderful things with lighting, like synchronizing the movement, color, and effects of multiple fixtures. Now our automated lights are getting smaller *and* brighter, lighter *and* cheaper, faster *and* more powerful.

In the past twenty years we have gone from using fixtures with five or six channels to fixtures with up to thirty-eight channels. Early fixtures had color and gobo wheels, pan and tilt, and not much more. Now we have fixtures with a host of effects including color *mixing,* rotating and indexable multi-colored glass gobos, remote focus, zoom, and lots of other effects including pan and tilt with three-phase stepper motors. At the same time, lighting manufacturers are using better materials like carbon fiber and injection molded or vacuum formed plastics to build stronger, lighter fixtures. New optical designs are improving fixture efficiency and improving the quality of projections with achromatic lenses, anti-reflective coating, multi-colored glass gobos, textured glass, and dichroic effects glass. Many fixture manufacturers are taking advantage of new lamp technology that significantly improves lamp life and efficiency. There are whole new arrays of fixtures on the market that use short-arc lamps and are benefiting from the greatly improved light output. Others are using lamps with higher color temperature, which appears to the human eye as a brighter field, and longer life, which greatly appeals to the pocketbook.

Advances in higher current handling switching devices have led to the increased use of electronic switching power supplies which are gradually replacing the heavier and less efficient magnetic ballast power supplies. And probably the most significant improvement has been the steady decrease in the price of similar fixtures. Sure, you can pay $10,000 or more for one state-of-the-art fixture, which is no doubt a lot of money. But you can also buy a fixture today for half the price of what you would have paid fifteen years ago, and the new fixture will have more effects and will be a lot smaller and brighter. You can also buy smaller, lower power fixtures today that weren't available fifteen years ago for a fraction of the price of anything that was available fifteen years ago.

Besides the heavy artillery, there are a host of accessories that have developed around the entertainment lighting industry. New wireless technology is being offered by Interactive Technologies (www.interactive-online.com) that eliminates the need for hard wiring a data homerun back to the console. ELC (www.elc-dmx.com) is manufacturing a wireless remote that interfaces with any DMX controller and allows the operator to preview scenes and test lights with a handheld remote. And both High End Systems and Interactive Technologies are marketing software for Palm™ handhelds that turn them into a fully programmable operating console.

On the other end of the data link, controllers and controller manufacturers are doing their part to hold up their end of the bargain. As one would expect, the lowering cost of computer hardware has translated into faster and more powerful consoles with lots of memory. But the most notable improvements have come in the area of software. There are a number of programming tools on the market today that can be used to shorten the design and programming process. WYSIWYG (www.castlighting.com) is a lighting design program that can be used for Computer Aided Design, off-line programming and editing, real-time visualization, and computer rendering of your show. LD Assistant AC has an AutoCAD engine and a fixture library that allows the user to quickly and easily design a lighting plot and render it in 3D. The Vari*Lite

Figure 1-1. Sydney Opera House and Harbour Bridge.
Lighting and technical design by Mr. Alan Stone. All equipment supplied by Coemar De Sisti Australia P/L. Rental Company - Clifton Productions. Programming by Megan McGahan.

List of equipment:
16 - Coemar CF1200 Hard Edge moving yoke fixtures
27 - Coemar CF1200 Wash moving yoke fixtures
15 - Coemar NAT 4000 15-30 degree zoom Mirror Movement fixtures
2 - Coemar NAT 4000 8-15 degree zoom Mirror Movement fixtures
9 - Coemar NAT 2500 Total Movement fixtures
10 - Coemar Panorama Cyc Architectural flood fixtures
18 - Condomes weatherproof covers
1 - Compulite Sabre control desk

Virtuoso console, which has now been discontinued, had the ability to address 26 universes of DMX and 2000 automated lights. It had a 3D interactive display that renders the lighting rig and beam projections in real-time.

Still, the lighting industry has an insatiable appetite for innovative new products. The victors in the business of lighting manufacturing are the ones who can build a new light a little bit brighter, or smaller, or lighter, or cheaper, or with unique effects. Those who fail to innovate languish in the marketplace.

But the battle for market share is the driving force behind most the advances in lighting technology. There is a healthy competition among entertainment lighting manufacturers that is heating up to the point of boiling over. In the next few years there will be a lot of consolidation as larger, more established lighting companies look for synergistic alliances with smaller, more nimble partners. Many architectural lighting manufacturers will seek to buy into automated lighting companies and their financial and technological infrastructure will no doubt create some interesting possibilities. Throw into the mix a flood of cheaper lighting technology and manufacturing capability from overseas and you have a volatile combination waiting to be set into motion.

Manufacturers live and die by how quickly they can get new products to market. One successful product might mean the difference between success and failure of the company. There are a lot more big bets these days because of the cost of R&D. Rapid prototyping technology such as stereo lithography (SLA) is helping to speed up the design process. The SLA process uses a UV laser to selectively cure an epoxy photopolymer into a solid object by mapping a 3D CAD file. At the same time, cheap labor from developing countries is lowering the barrier to entry into the professional lighting market. Products from Asia and the former Soviet Republic countries are producing goods that are on par with anything the developed countries are producing.

But surely there will be a few potholes on the road to "smaller, brighter, lighter, cheaper and faster." One of the most promising products being developed in the past few years was the Icon M. It is a moving yoke fixture that used an array of Digital Mirror Devices (DMD) made by Texas Instruments. The fixture held the promise of soft gobos that could be loaded onto the fixture by using graphics tools. Ultimately the challenges of managing the heat produced by the fixture proved to be too great and the project was scrapped.

In 2000 High End Systems introduced 'Catalyst', which is their answer to the Icon M. Catalyst is an orbital moving mirror that mounts onto the front of a video projector and moves video images in a 360° by 180° area. It allows the operator to use a conventional lighting console to manipulate a catalog of soft gobos and images including live video.

The computer industry is supplying the enabling technology for the lighting industry and we are the beneficiaries of their research and development, hardware and software production, and application of technology. But our current approach to manufacturing integrated circuit chips is about to reach its limit. The lithographic process in which we use photomasks to etch and dope microscopic circuits onto a substrate can provide only so much resolution. After we reach a certain point we cannot continue to reduce the scale of the circuits. Therefore we cannot produce the faster, smaller, higher-density computer chips as we have been for the past forty years. Some people think we will reach this limit in about ten years.

So what's next? Scientists and engineers are now working on the development of a new technology, called nanotechnology, that will enable the production of integrated circuits with components that are just 10 nanometers in diameter or one hundred times smaller than the diameter of a human hair. These IC chips will be built atom by atom and will be much faster and higher in density than current technology allows. Instead of using photomasking techniques, these circuits will be organically grown by building layers of conducting material, rather than removing and doping material. Nanotechnology could be a commercial reality in the next ten to fifteen years.

At the end of the last millennium, optimism abounded about the future of technology. It was almost euphoria and it was reflected in the stock market. In 1999, the NASDAQ (www.nasdaq.com), which is the market for tech stocks, advanced 88% - a huge gain by usual standards. Since then the market has crashed back down to earth and the technology sector has been especially hard hit. But that is no reflection on the rapid development of technology or the state of its future. The market is driven by other, often-unrelated phenomenon such as consumer sentiment and optimism. Sometimes there is no explanation at all. Such is the nature of the stock market. Technology is much more predictable. It advances each and every day.

We have every reason to believe that the lighting industry will be an exciting place to be in the foreseeable future. If history is any indicator, then we can safely assume that there will never be a dull moment. With new electronics technology, better optics, space-age materials and improved manufacturing techniques, we have everything to gain. At the pace we're going, we will need more and more people who understand the technology and the industry to help maintain the infrastructure to support the industry.

Turn on the lights; the party's just begun.

2 GENERATION DMX

"To attain knowledge, add things every day. To attain wisdom, remove things every day."
– Lao-tzu, Chinese philosopher of the sixth century B.C.

There was a time not long ago that if you were describing a digital data protocol, you might have to explain what is meant by "digital". Today I suppose that under the same circumstances, you might have to explain that there used to be something other than digital – something called "analog" – which was commonly used in electronics for a variety of applications. As incredible as it may sound to some, there was a time, not *that* long ago, when many lighting consoles used a proportional 0-10 volt dc signal to control dimmers. If this is foreign to you then you are a true Generation DMX'er.

DMX512 is the digital data protocol that has effectively replaced analog control; much the same way that my 8-track tape collection has been replaced by CD's. And much the same way Advance Control Network (ACN), or some version of it, will someday replace DMX. Whatever the future might hold, we are now firmly entrenched in a digital environment.

A digital signal is not a complicated one. It has exactly two values – a high state and a low state. The trick is to switch between the two states incredibly fast and incredibly accurately – the way only a computer can. By encoding the data and transmitting it at a high rate of speed, a single pair of wires can transmit enough DMX information to control 512 channels.

Binary Building Blocks

We're a base ten society. Most everything we've been taught about math since the time we could count is based on the ten digits we call the decimal system. We use ten digits, zero through nine, to represent any number using a combination of those ten digits and a decimal point. Each place to the left of the decimal point represents a value of a power of ten.

For example, the number 2,371 = $(2 \times 10^3) + (3 \times 10^2) + (7 \times 10^1) + (1 \times 10^0)$.

$10^0 = 1$
$10^1 = 10$
$10^2 = 100$
$10^3 = 1000$
$10^4 = 10{,}000$

Binary, on the other hand, is a base two numbering system. There are only two digits, zero and one. With those two numbers we can represent any number as well as we can with the decimal system. Each place represents a value of a power of two.

$2^0 = 1$
$2^1 = 2$
$2^2 = 4$
$2^3 = 8$
$2^4 = 16$

As an example, the number 2,371 in base ten can be represented in binary, or base two by the following:

$100101000011 = (1 \times 2^{11}) + (0 \times 2^{10}) + (0 \times 2^9) + (1 \times 2^8) + (0 \times 2^7) + (1 \times 2^6) + (0 \times 2^5) + (0 \times 2^4) + (0 \times 2^3) + (0 \times 2^2) + (1 \times 2^1) + (1 \times 2^0)$

By adding up the value of each place we arrive at the final number. The table below shows binary equivalents to the base ten numbers we are used to seeing.

Binary	Decimal	Binary	Decimal	Binary	Decimal
0	0	1010	10	10100	20
1	1	1011	11	10101	21
10	2	1100	12	10110	22
11	3	1101	13	10111	23
100	4	1110	14	11000	24
101	5	1111	15	11001	25
110	6	10000	16	11010	26
111	7	10001	17	11011	27
1000	8	10010	19	11100	28
1001	9	10011	19	11101	29

My third eye senses that I'm reaching the limits of your patience with math. Besides, what's all this have to do with lighting anyway?

512, 513, Whatever It Takes

The answer is that DMX512 is a binary protocol. You'll notice that certain numbers keep appearing again and again in the digital realm. After all, where did the “512” in “DMX512” come from? It’s not “DMX511” or “DMX513”, but “DMX512.” That’s because 512 is a power of two, or 2^9. It’s a round number in binary. Also, there are 256 steps of level information in each DMX channel. That’s because the information is packaged in eight-bit bytes, which yields 256 unique combinations of zeros and ones.

For dimming and most other functions, 256 are plenty of steps to give you the illusion of continuous or analog output. But for pan and tilt, the typical automated moving light pans at least 180° and tilts at least 90°. If you do the math (don’t worry, I’ll do it for you) you’ll find that dividing 180° by 256 steps yields a 3.7” (9.4cm) step at a throw distance of 50’ (15.24m). That means that the absolute smallest movement possible is almost four inches. That’s not exactly in the realm of analog. To make matters even worse, many fixtures now have the capability to pan 540°, which yields an ugly 11” (27.94cm) step at 50’ (15.24m). Such low resolution produces jagged movements, especially when moving diagonally. But fear not, because most manufacturers of automated lighting have rewritten their channel assignments to enable the use of two DMX channels for each axis of movement. That’s called 16-bit resolution because it uses two eight-bit bytes for one control parameter. Thus, the pan and tilt channels each have 32,768 steps available for the full range of motion. That’s far more analog-like.

A DMX signal looks like a square wave with various duty cycles. Each interval represents a binary 0 or 1. The group of eight bits that provide level information is embedded in a packet with additional bits.

Back in my day we used to have to set DIP (dual in-line) switches to configure a DMX address. We used to have to carry around a binary number chart or add up the numbers on our fingers or with a slide rule to figure out the settings. Then you would have to turn on and off these miniature switches, which would be a lot easier if you had miniature hands and miniature fingers. DMX’ers these days don’t know how easy they have it with menu displays.

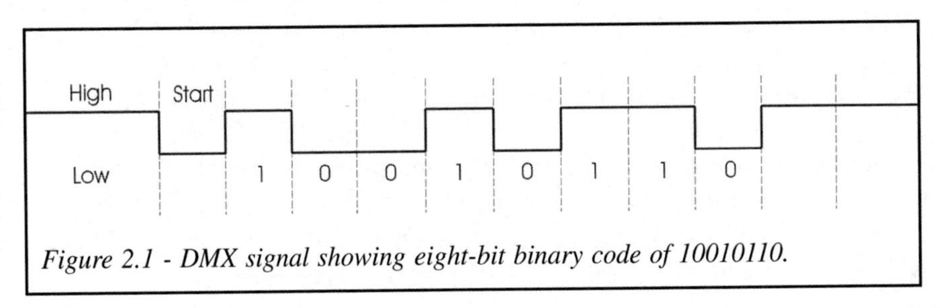

Figure 2.1 - DMX signal showing eight-bit binary code of 10010110.

Decoding DMX

The code that goes streaming down a DMX data cable is a series of voltage levels – high and low – that our system interprets as zeros and ones. On a deeper level, we have encoded the system to group those zero's and one's in such a fashion as to carry significance. The significance of the DMX data is that it tells the receiver exactly what to do and when to do it. A standard was devised by USITT in order that any console could produce DMX data, which in turn could be interpreted by any other DMX device. The data contains information about the dimmer levels for 512 channels, arranged in little packages called bytes. In DMX, a byte is 11-bits worth of data, or eleven crunchy little zero's and one's. The first bit is the start bit, which is always a low state, or a logic zero. The next eight bits contain the dimmer level information. Remember that with eight bits you can represent 256 different numbers ($2^8 = 256$) or levels of information. The last two bits are the stop bits, which are always high, or a logic one. These eleven bits are referred to as one frame.

Even though we might refer to it as a dimmer level, the information can control any parameter that we choose. It might be the pan or tilt position, a color or gobo, or it could be a fog machine output level. It doesn't matter. What does matter is that we are able to accurately control some device with a digital signal while we eat a sandwich or talk on the cell phone.

But before we can transmit the dimmer level information, there is some housekeeping to do. The first task of the data transmission is to alert the receiver that it is starting transmission. Otherwise it would not know where to begin and it would just be a continuous stream of zero's and one's marching toward infinity with no real purpose in life (remember your college days?). Instead, the "Break" signal tells the receiver that the next chunk of data coming its way is going to contain the dimmer level information for the first of 512 channels. It does this by holding the voltage to the low level for a minimum of 88 microseconds (μsec or 10^{-6} seconds). A microsecond is one millionth of a second. That gives you an indication of just how precise of a time period we are dealing with here, which is exactly what computers are good at – counting precisely, accurately, and quickly. But, of course, it can only count to one. *Zero, one, remember?*

The break is always followed by something called the "Mark-After-Break" or M.A.B., when the voltage is taken high for at least 8 μsec. So far, we have the Break, which signifies the start of a packet, then the Mark-After-Break, which signifies the end of the Break. But wait, it gets better.

The next part of the packet after the M.A.B. is the "Start-Code." The Start-Code is an eleven-bit byte, which tells the receiver what type of data is to follow. The only currently defined type of data that is allowed in DMX is 8-bit level information. That is signified by a Start-Code of zero (00000000). Any other value in the Start-Code is not currently recognized by standard DMX protocol, but some manufacturers use non-zero values for proprietary reasons. In the future, the DMX standard could be amended to include the use of non-zero values in the Start-Code. For now, there are none. The Start-Code is referenced in the USITT standard as the Null Start Code because the only defined value is the null set, or zero. It took me a few readings to get that, but then, I'm still trying to figure out the Electoral College.

Once the housekeeping is taken care of and we have marked the beginning and alerted the receiver that the information it is about to receive is dimmer level data, then the real fun begins. The dimmer level information is then transmitted in sequential order, starting with the first address and on through the last. The first frame is transmitted corresponding to the dimmer level for channel one, the second for channel two and so on. The entire sequence from the break until the last channel of dimmer level information is transmitted is called a packet. After the entire packet is transmitted, the transmitter can then start over and transmit an updated packet with current dimmer level information.

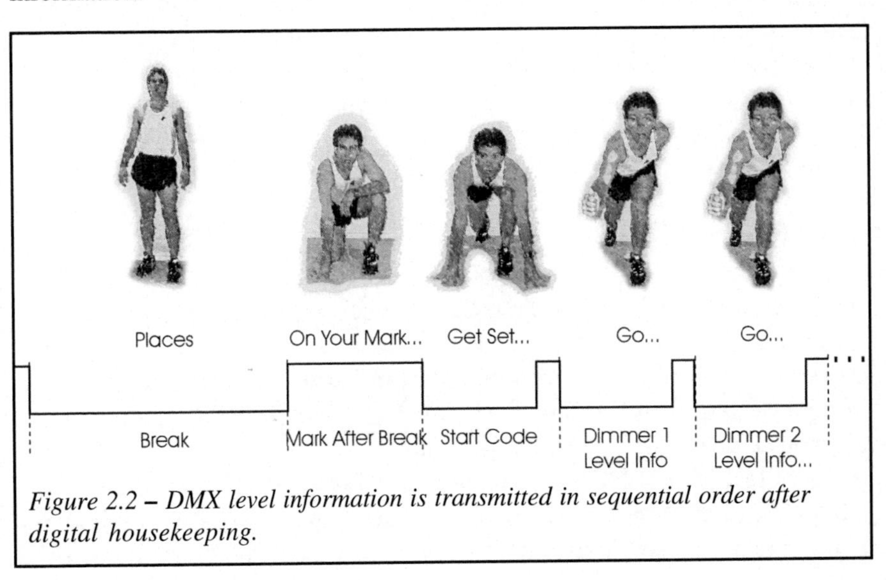

Figure 2.2 – DMX level information is transmitted in sequential order after digital housekeeping.

Each bit is transmitted at a rate of 4 μsec. That means that a DMX transmitter can transmit 250,000 bits per second (1 sec x 4μsec per bit = 250,000 bits per second), or 250 kilobaud. An entire packet with 512 channels is 5,643 bits (512 channels x 11 bits per byte, plus 11 bits for the start code). The transmission time for the whole packet is 22,668 μsec (5,643 bits x 4 μsec per bit, plus 88 μsec for the Break and 8 μsec for the Mark-After-Break). That means that in one second, the transmitter can transmit 44.115 packets (1 second x 22,668 μsec per packet = 44.115 packets per second). So the maximum *refresh rate* is 44.115.

There are all manner of rules about the timing and idle states that the transmitter has to follow, which we won't get into. These standards committees are freaks about order, and thankfully so. When we want to use one manufacturer's console with another manufacturer's lighting load, we don't have to purchase a proprietary interface as long as they are both DMX compliant. I wish the remotes for my television, VCR, cable, stereo, and garage door opener were as easy to integrate.

DMX Cable

Capacitance is a funny thing. You can't see it, hear it, feel it, taste it or smell it. But you can see the effects of it. Even when you don't want to. And there are apparently two varieties of capacitance. There's something called "stray" capacitance, which implies there's also a more domesticated variety.

When I was taking my freshman electronics lab course, we used to have to build breadboard analog circuits and test them. We were asked to measure the specs, things like impedence, gain, performance and all manner of fun things. The test results never matched the expected performance. They always varied from the theoretical design. We had to write up reports in our lab notebook and explain the results, good or bad. Invariably, I would explain away the deviations as "stray capacitance." Stray capacitance is caused by long wires and long leads on components. It became my academic salvation. If ever there was a problem I would play the stray capacitance card. Wrong impedence? Oh, that was because of the "stray capacitance." Wrong frequency? Yep, stray capacitance. Overslept? Must have been some stray capacitance in the alarm clock this morning.

Capacitance is a bit like the weather. We can predict it and prepare for it, but it's difficult to control. You can build a capacitor by sandwiching an insulator between two conductors. It can be two metal plates separated by a polymer, or it can be aluminum coated Mylar rolled into a cylindrical shape. It can even be two copper wires coated with rubber insulation. It might even be a twisted pair of insulated wires with braided wire shield. Sound familiar? I just described a cable, much like the cable used for audio, video, and data transmission. A cable is a type of capacitor. It acts exactly like a resistor in series and a capacitor in parallel.

A capacitor stores energy. As you apply voltage to it, it gradually "fills up" with charged electrons and holds them until it sees an opportunity to discharge them. In high school some of the more excitable kids in my electronics class used to charge up capacitors and toss them down the hall at innocent hall wanderers. They hoped that someone would pick up the capacitor and get zapped from the discharge. Fortunately, the culprits didn't have access to high voltage capacitors that could have done serious harm. You buy them books and send them to school, and what do they do? They eat the covers.

The value of the capacitor determines how quickly the capacitor will charge and how fast the voltage across it will rise to match the applied voltage. The

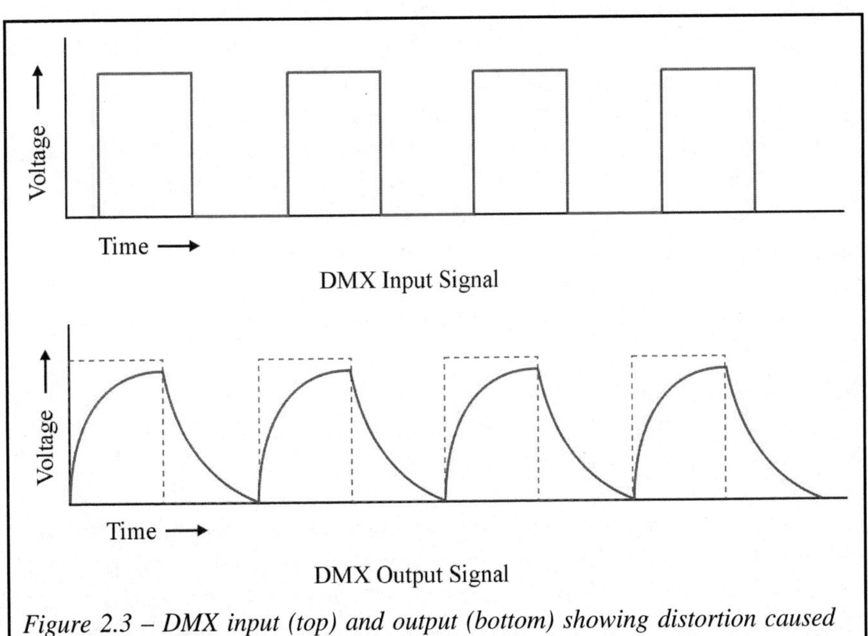

Figure 2.3 – DMX input (top) and output (bottom) showing distortion caused by high capacitance cable. Signal degredation can garble data and cause inaccurate readings and data errors.

higher the capacitance, the slower the voltage will rise. When you apply a data signal like DMX to a cable, the source sees a load that looks like a resistor in series and a capacitor across the output. The value of the capacitance depends on the construction of the cable. There are all sorts of factors that influence the characteristic capacitance of the cable, such as the type and size of the insulation and the type of shield it has.

A DMX signal is a series of square waves, or simply a voltage quickly switching on and off across the cable. If the cable has a high characteristic capacitance it resists the change in voltage and badly distorts the square wave. It makes it look more like a sawtooth wave than a square wave. Low capacitance cable, on the other hand, helps maintain the integrity of high frequency signals.

At first glance microphone cable looks just like data transmission cable. It comes in twisted pairs and has a nicely braided shield. But if you examine the specs you'll see that it has a relatively high value of capacitance. It makes little difference to an audio signal because the frequency of the audible range is far below that of the DMX baud rate. Low frequencies are relatively unaffected by high capacitance. The voltage isn't changing as quickly, so the capacitor doesn't resist the change as much. Audio signals don't care much about capacitance. DMX signals live and die by capacitance.

Data cable has a low capacitance and is made specifically for data transmission. It might cost more than low impedence cable and it's not as readily available. You might have to source it somewhere other than the Radio Shack down the street. In "Recommended Practice for DMX512 – A guide for users and installers" by Adam Bennette (published by PLASA and USITT) there are a variety of recommended cables made by Belden, Alpha Wire, and Proplex (distributed by TMB – www.tmb.com). AC Lighting (www.aclighting.com in the U.S. or www.aclighting.co.uk in the U.K.) and Creative Stage Lighting (www.creativestagelighting.com) also distribute excellent quality data cable under the trade names Tourplex and Duraflex, respectively.

Buy data cable for data transmission. All it takes is time and money. But think about how much time and money you save when you avoid problems with inferior data cables. I've seen countless "mysterious" problems that were caused by nothing more than high capacitance cable. The frustrating thing is that you can't see, hear, taste, touch or feel the problem. After all, the cable *looks* like it is working. It tests okay with a continuity checker. It provides a good solid connection and there are no cold solder joints. Yet it will make automated lights wig out. The cable will probably even work okay if the system is small with short runs and few lights. But when you start adding fixtures to the system, they misbehave. They act strangely, moving for no reason, doing things they shouldn't do. The only way you can see the problem is to use an oscilloscope to look at the distortion in the signal. Or you could avoid the problem altogether and buy the proper data cable. All it takes is time and money.

There's enough stray capacitance in this world without inviting the more domesticated variety to live in your data system. Buy and use data cable that is designed to work correctly with DMX data and you won't have to explain your bad results.

3 ADVANCED CONTROL NETWORK

"The masters of technology will have to be lighthearted and intelligent. The machine easily masters the grim and the dumb."
– Marshall McLuhan

Where is the lighting industry headed in this crazy, topsy-turvy world in which we live? Look no further than the computer industry and the internet and you'll find gigabytes of clues. We're being sucked into the vacuum left by the rapid advance of the internet and computer technology. Nowhere is it more evident than by the next generation control protocol currently under development by the ESTA Control Protocols Task Group.

The Advanced Control Network, or ACN as it is being dubbed, will eventually replace DMX as the standard for distribution of data in lighting control networks. It is, as its moniker implies, far more advanced than DMX and it will not only make it easier to interconnect various brands of controlled devices, it will also provide many more benefits over DMX. Among them is the ability to interconnect a multitude of devices that can all "speak" to each other and operate as a system.

Does that sound a bit like the internet to you? It should. The new protocol will be based on the TCP/IP (Transmission Control Protocol/Internet Protocol), and to use off-the-shelf hardware and software such as routers, switches, and hubs that are commonly used in computer networks. You may have seen a reference to TCP/IP if you've ever played with or configured your computer for the internet or e-mail. Charles Hedrick in Introduction to the Internet Protocols describes TCP/IP[1]. "TCP/IP is a set of protocols developed to allow cooperating computers to share resources across a network." TCP and IP are actually two of the protocols in the suite, but "because TCP and IP are the best known of the protocols, it has become common to use the term TCP/IP or IP/TCP to refer to the whole family." Think of them as a suite of software, much like Microsoft Office (Word, Excel, etc.), each of which performs a unique and specific function related to a common goal. In this case, the goal is to communicate control information in a meaningful way.

In some ways, ACN will provide the same functions as DMX. It will control lighting and effects by way of digital communication. In other ways, it will be better. For example, it will provide for multiple sources of control data on the same network. So instead of having one console for your conventional lighting on a network and another console for your moving lights on a separate network, they could be interconnected and operate together on one data line. Or, in a theatre environment where you might normally disconnect the data output from the main console and plug in a remote controller for preset focus, you would have them both online at the same time on the same network. That feature alone might give you more time for coffee and doughnuts.

ACN will also be a "scalable" protocol, meaning that the network will handle the smallest systems as well as the largest systems. There will be no limits on the number of addresses it can handle. It will not be ACN-512 or ACN-1024, but just plain ACN, implying infinite connectivity. In addition, it will be a "plug and play" network where each of the devices on the network has the ability to discover and identify one another without user intervention. No longer will you have to set the address of a fixture, or worse yet, fly a rig only to discover that the address settings have not been configured. If you have ever added a peripheral to Windows 95 or 98, then you know how cool this feature can be. If not, take my word for it. You'll learn to love it.

The protocol, naturally, is being designed to support audio control and stage automation. I think it's a natural step because it seems the entire world is being networked, including your cell phone, your PDA, and even your refrigerator. Why not throw in the kitchen sink? I recently read an article in Sound & Communications magazine about video projector software that InFocus is developing to be internet ready. No doubt there is a lot of behind the scenes work to do to establish common ground between the different disciplines involved. But count on having to be nice to the sound geeks and video freaks, at least for load in and set up.

Finally, the protocol will support feedback from the devices on the system. So the fixtures are supposed to be able to talk to the controller just as the controller now talks to the fixtures. However, this is a potential sticking point since Vari-Lite (www.vari-lite.com) owns a patent that refers to a bi-directional data link in a moving light system. U.S. Patent 5,010,459 covers the control of moving lights and the communications link between the controller and the fixtures, including transmitting signals to, and receiving signals from the fixtures. For more detailed information about the patent check out the U.S. Patent and Trademark Office web site at http://www.uspto.gov/patft/

index.html and search for the above patent number.

Will the proposed ACN standard infringe on Vari-Lite's patent? In the case of dimmers and effects, probably not. In the case of moving lights who's to say? A judge? A jury? I think it can be argued either way, and if that argument happens to be in a court of law it might literally cost millions of dollars to find out the answer. Vari-Lite has demonstrated their willingness to defend their patents in a court of law on at least four separate cases: once against the now defunct Summa Technologies, once against Synchrolite, once against High End Systems, and once against Martin Professional. The Synchrolite and High End cases were both settled out of court and Summa went out of business before their lawsuit could be settled. Thus no precedents were set. But just about every technological achievement these days has to work through some patent issues in order to stand on the shoulders of its predecessors. Legal issues are just part of the terrain. However, according to Rusty Brutsché, Chairman and CEO, Vari-Lite is "working with the ESTA on the standard and we are dealing with the patent issues as they arise." It is, after all, in the best interest of everyone involved to advance the protocol to the next level. The manufacturers that I have talked to have all said that they don't want to end up with a proprietary protocol, but would rather have something that cuts across manufacturers boundaries. Does Vari-Lite agree? Stay tuned and find out.

In the meanwhile, you can find out more information about ACN from the ESTA web site at www.esta.org. Click on Technical Standards Program, Control Protocols, and finally Advanced Control Protocol under Task Group Projects. Also, for an excellent article written by Steve Carlson and the ACN Task Group describing ACN in more detail, see the Winter 2000 issue of *Protocol*, the journal of the Entertainment Services & Technology Association.

About three hundred years ago, German mathematician Gottfried Leibniz and English physicist and astronomer Sir Isaac Newton invented calculus at the same time completely independent of one another. In much the same manner, the computer, lighting, audio, video, and other industries are converging and coming to the same conclusion. The conclusion? There just might be something to this networking/internet thing.

---

[1] Copyright © 1987 by Charles L. Hedrick, Computer Science Facilities Group, Rutgers University. Used by permission. For more info, see gopher://gopher-chem.ucdavis.edu/11/Index/Internet_aw/Intro_the_Internet/intro.to.ip/

4 WHAT TEMPERATURE IS THAT COLOR?

"If you cannot measure it, you cannot improve it."
– Lord Kelvin (1824-1907), British mathematician and physicist.

When I first started learning about lighting, I had a hard time understanding the simple concept of color temperature. I was reading a great little reference book called *The Sylvania/GTE Lighting Handbook*[1], and it was describing something called a blackbody radiator. Former Washington Redskins quarterback Joe Theisman is rumored to have said, "A genius is a guy like Norman Einstein." I'm no "Norman" Einstein, let's make no mistake about that. But, in college I studied such esoteric subjects as thermodynamics and vector calculus and I didn't have as much trouble as I did with blackbody radiators. After reading several different sources on the topic, I finally came to grips with the concept and how it works. One of the best resources on this and almost every other lighting subject is *The IESNA Lighting Handbook*[2].

Figure 4-1. The Visible Spectrum showing component colors that make up white light.

Let's explore color temperature and see if we can do it without using the "blackbody" word.

Color temperature is a way of quantifying the quality of light, or assigning a number to the "color" of white light. The number relates to the balance between red and blue, the two opposite ends of the visible light spectrum. You may have noticed that some white light is whiter than other white light. It's not always easy to tell because the human eye has an uncanny ability to adjust for deficiencies in the spectral balance of white light. But if you compare two sources of light side by side, then the differences are a lot easier to see. For example, have you noticed the halogen headlights in some of the newer cars recently? When you're driving at night and you see a line of cars coming toward you, it's easy to pick out the halogen lights. They have a blue-ish color and seem brighter by contrast.

The concept of color temperature is derived from Planck's law of radiation. Max Planck was a German physicist who, in 1899, developed a formula that describes the distribution of brightness in the spectrum of a body that is radiating light. The formula links the intensity of a given wavelength, or color, to the temperature of the object. What it tells us is that for a given temperature, the content of each color in the visible spectrum can be found. Stars radiate light because they are extremely hot. By using Planck's law of radiation, scientists can determine the temperature of a star by examining the distribution of brightness in the spectrum of the light that is emitted by that star. In other words, they use the light from a star to determine its temperature. Lighting professionals, on the other hand, do it the other way around. We use the temperature as a specification that tells us the "color" of white light.

If you are having a problem, as I once did, understanding Planck's law and how it relates to lighting specs, then consider this. If you put a metal poker in a fire and steadily increase the temperature, what would happen? As the metal started incandescing and continued to rise in temperature, it would go through a series of color changes. It would start by glowing red, and then it would progress through orange, yellow, white, then blue-ish white. Why does the light change color? Because as the temperature increases, the light energy is distributed differently throughout the visible spectrum. How the light is scattered throughout the spectrum is referred to as the spectral power distribution or the SPD.

Since scientists invented the concept, they used a scale that is very common in the scientific community - the Kelvin temperature scale. The Kelvin is based

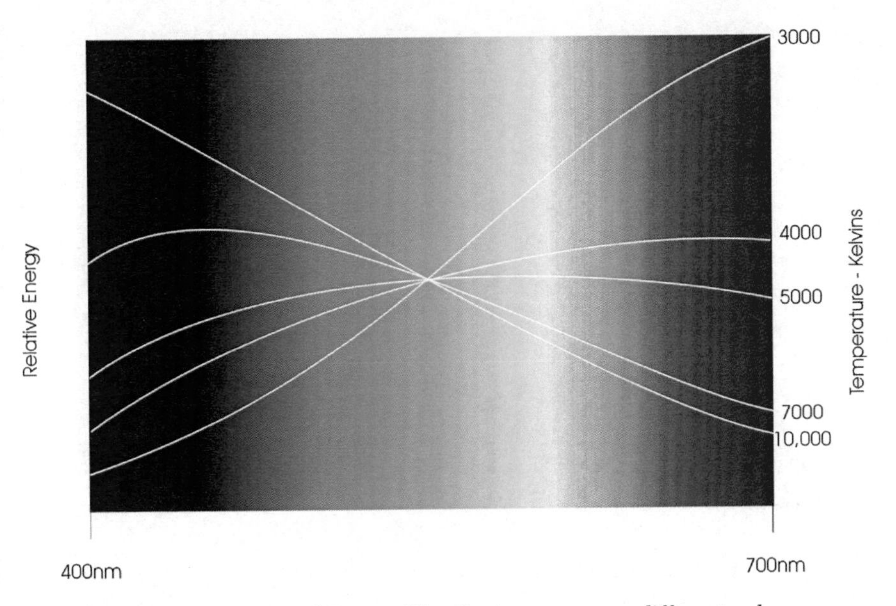

Figure 4-2. Relative Spectral Power Distribution curves at different color temperatures.

on the Celsius temperature system (0° C is the temperature at which water freezes and 100°C is the temperature at which water boils) with an offset of -273°C. The reason for that is because all molecular motion stops at that temperature and it is called "absolute" zero. So -273°C is the same as 0°K, which is absolute zero. The Kelvin scale is named after its inventor, Lord Kelvin (William Thomson), a Scottish physicist and mathematician.

Natural sunlight is pretty well balanced between the red and the blue end of the visible light spectrum. Artificial light, on the other hand, is not always so well balanced. An incandescent lamp, for example, contains much more light energy in the red end of the spectrum than in the blue. An incandescent lamp is any lamp with a filament. The filament, usually made of tungsten, passes an electrical current through it. The natural resistance of the filament causes it to heat up so intensely that it gives off light. The color temperature of an incandescent lamp ranges from about 2500K to about 3200K. Most PAR cans, Lekos, and cyc lights have incandescent sources. Because it has little light energy in the blue end of the spectrum, an incandescent lamp is not a great source to use for UV and indigo colors. They are much better at producing reds, yellows, and oranges. Is it possible to increase the

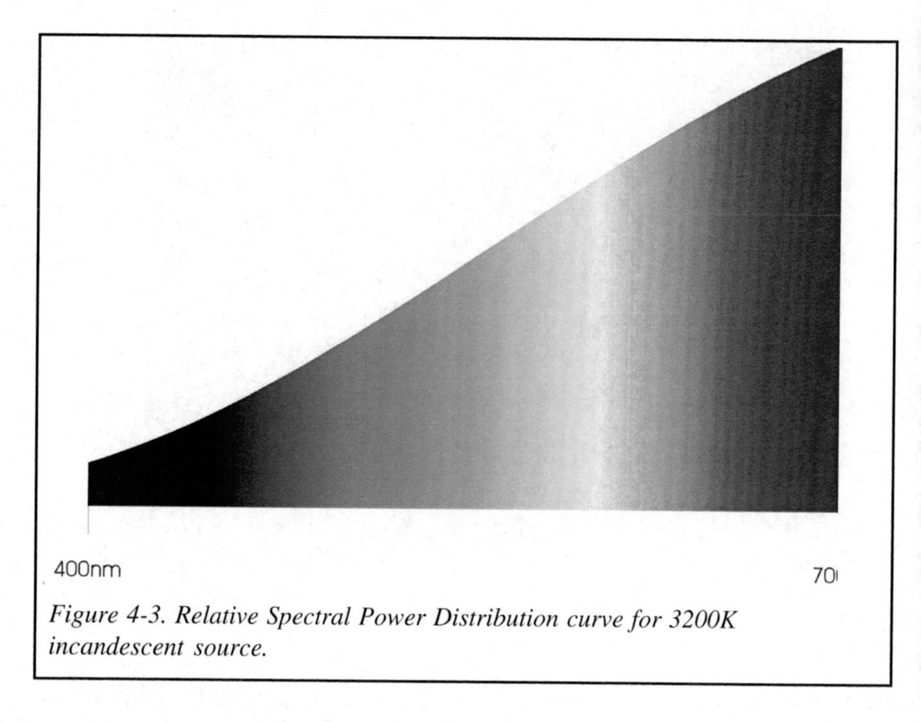

Figure 4-3. Relative Spectral Power Distribution curve for 3200K incandescent source.

temperature of an incandescent lamp beyond 3200K? I don't believe so. Since the melting point of tungsten is about 3683°K, it's not practical with current technology.

For higher color temperatures, we have to rely on different lamp technology such as arc lamps, or we have to use color filters. As you go up in color temperature, the light energy moves away from the red end of the spectrum and towards the blue. At around 5500K, the light energy is very well balanced between the red and blue ends of the spectrum. It closely matches natural sunlight. As the temperature increases even higher, the bulk of the light energy shifts to the blue end of the spectrum and away from the red. The white light produced by a very high color temperature source appears blue-ish. Xenon lamps are a good example of a lamp with a very high color temperature, typically around 6400K.

White light is made up of every color in the visible spectrum.[3] But not all light sources produce a nice continuous spectrum with every color of the rainbow. Some light sources, like arc lamps, only produce a few different wavelengths in the spectrum. But the human eye has an amazing ability to "average" the given wavelengths and fill in the gaps to give us the impression that the entire spectrum is there. We can equate the quality of that type of light to the color temperature of a continuous spectrum lamp. This is referred to as the "correlated" color temperature. Most of the time that you read about a color temperature of an arc lamp, they are actually referring to the correlated color temperature.

If you have sources with different color temperatures and you want to match them, then you can use color correction filters. For example, if you have PAR cans and moving lights with arc lamps, then you'll want to either correct your PAR's from 3200K to 5600K (or whatever the color temperature of your arc lamps is) or you'll want to correct your moving lights to 3200K. Standard filters are available to correct from daylight to incandescent and visa versa. A CTO, or "correct to orange" filter is used to shift the color temperature from daylight to incandescent. A CTB, or "correct to blue" is used to shift from incandescent to daylight.

As a lighting professional, there are many things that you need to know about color temperature. Fortunately for me, blackbody radiators are not one of them. All you really need to know is how to read a lamp spec and understand how that spec affects the quality of the light from that particular lamp source.

---

[1] The Sylvania GTE Lighting Handbook was last published in 1989 after the eight printings. I highly recommend it if you can find a copy.

[2] Published by the Illuminating Engineering Society of North America (www.iesna.org).

[3] For a handy reference chart, check out the Solar Spectrum Chart from Edmund Scientific. It's a full color chart of the solar spectrum, which just happens to coincide pretty closely with the visible spectrum. They are available online at www.edmundscientific.com for $15.95.

5 APPLES TO APPLES

"The universe is a grand book which cannot be read until one first learns to comprehend the language and become familiar with the characters in which it is composed. It is written in the language of mathematics."
– Galileo

One of the things that you can count on in the lighting industry is that claims will be made about how bright a particular light is. "Our lights are brighter than your lights," or "This light is brighter than that light." It's as certain as the sun will rise in the east and a lot more frequent. All kinds of specifications are written to support these claims and photometric data in a variety of forms will be published to make you think that there is no finer luminaire this side of the sun. How many times have you heard this; "50% brighter!" or "Twice as bright!"

But how can you know which is brighter, especially when you see so many different ways or representing photometric data? The data can be in the form of a chart, showing illumination levels and beam angles at specified distances, or it can be in the form of a single value of luminous flux plus the beam or field angle. Or it might even be in the form of luminous intensity plus the beam or field angle.

The best way to know how to interpret this data is to arm yourself with knowledge and to be able to use and convert these quantities into any and every form.

Art Imitates Light

Let's say that light is like paint, and lighting a set is like painting a canvass. Then we can make the following associations:

a) A bare lamp is like a bucket of paint
b) A luminaire or fixture that the lamp goes in is like a paint brush or air compressor and air gun
c) The beam angle is like the width of the brush stroke
d) Illumination is like the thickness of the paint on the canvas

The first lighting metric we want to learn about is called the *total luminous flux*. It's a measure of the total quantity of light that is emitted from a lamp source in all directions. It is measured in lumens. Think of the total luminous flux as the quantity of paint in the bucket. It tells us how much paint we have, which is important if we want to know how well it will cover the canvass or how many buckets we'll need to paint the canvass to meet a certain criteria for the thickness of the paint. The total luminous flux is usually provided on the spec sheet for the lamp.

Not all of the light produced by a lamp makes it out of the front lens of the fixture. In the process of pouring the paint from the bucket into the reservoir of the compressor, some of it sticks to the side of the bucket and some spills on the ground. Some of it never makes it to the nozzle of the air gun. In much the same manner, not all of the light from the lamp source is collected by the reflector. Some of it is scattered inside the fixture and some is leaked out of the air vents. Some of it is lost to the inefficiencies of the lenses, filters, gobos, and effects. The optical system is not 100% efficient. That leads us to our first conclusion:

Not all optical systems are created equal

Some are more efficient than others. Don't assume that because two fixtures have identical lamp sources that they also have similar light output. Put them to the test.

Putting Luminaires to the Test

Testing the light output of a luminaire normally involves the next lighting metric that we want to learn about. The *illumination* is a measure of the amount of light striking a surface and it is measured in footcandles or lux. In the English system of measurements where we measure the throw distance and area of coverage in feet, illumination is measured in footcandles. In the metric system we use meters and lux. Think of illumination as the thickness of the paint on a canvass. Since we have a limited amount of paint, the amount of paint we apply to the canvass is integrally tied to the size of the canvass. The thicker we apply the paint, the smaller the area we can cover with one bucket of paint. They are inextricably linked. What's more, the relationship between the two is exponential. If we double the size of the canvass from, say, from 2 meters x 2 meters to 4 meters x 4 meters, then we quadruple the area that we're covering (4 square meters to 16 square meters). Therefore, the area of the canvass is exponentially related to the thickness of the paint applied (assuming we have a limited amount of paint to work with). The same can be said in terms of lighting. That is,

The intensity of illumination of a luminaire is inversely and exponentially proportional to the area covered

If you double the throw distance of a fixture then you will decrease the illumination on the surface by a factor of four. Similarly, if you change the beam angle of a fixture, the illumination will change exponentially.

Let's say you have two fixtures with which you want to compare brightness. One of them uses a Plutonium 1000 lamp and the other uses a Nitroglycerin 1000 lamp. You check the lamp specs and find that they both produce 5×10^4 initial lumens, thanks to the new low-radiation tabletop fusion technology. One of the fixtures, the P1000, has a beam angle of 16° while the other, the N1000, has a beam angle of 24°. You line them up side-by-side, and project them 10 meters onto a nice clean white cyc. You get out your tape measure, your light meter, and your calculator – or your slide rule if you want to be nostalgic about it. Here's what you find:

Fixture A produces a beam 2.81 meters in diameter. The illumination at the center of the beam is 1815 lux. Fixture B produces a beam 4.25 meters in diameter. The illumination at the center of the beam is 838 lux.

Assuming perfect beam uniformity, which fixture has more light output? Let's see...fixture A with 1815 lux versus fixture B with 838 lux. The answer is Fixture B. Why? Because Fixture B is illuminating a larger area. To verify that statement, we can work backwards and find the total luminous flux of both fixtures (as opposed to the lamps). The total luminous flux (l) is the illumination (i) multiplied by the area covered (a)[1]. First we calculate the area by using the formula for the area of a circle, which is pi (3.14...) times the square of the radius:

For Fixture A, Area *(a)* = pi *x* radius²

$$a = 3.14 \times (2.81)^2$$

$$a = 24.8$$

For Fixture B, Area *(a)* = pi *x* radius^2

$$a = 3.14 \times (4.25)^2$$

$$a = 56.7$$

Then we calculate the total luminous flux for each fixture:

For Fixture A, total luminous flux *(l)* = illumination *(i)* x area *(a)*

$$l = 1815 \times 24.8$$

$$l = 45{,}012 \text{ lux}$$

For Fixture B, total luminous flux *(l)* = illumination *(i)* x area *(a)*

$$l = 838 \times 56.7$$

$$l = 47{,}514 \text{ lux}$$

So you can clearly see that Fixture B is indeed outputting more light than Fixture A. If you only look at the illumination without regard to the size of the spot the fixture is producing, you could mistakenly conclude that Fixture A has more light output than Fixture B. The proper way to compare them would be to place the fixtures so that they produce the same size beam on the wall. One fixture might be closer to the wall than the other, but the important thing is that they are covering the same area.

Notice that in this entire discussion never once was the word "wattage" mentioned. That's because wattage is a measure of electrical power and has nothing to do with light output. That leads us to our final conclusion:

Wattage is *not* a measure of light output

Never confuse the two and never refer to the light output in relation to watts. The answer to the question "How much light does this fixture produce?" never ends with the word "watts."

If you are going to compare to fixtures, it's only fair to make sure they both have new lamps, since the light output degrades over time. It's also a good idea to check that the lamps are aligned in their fixtures properly.

Once you understand lighting metrics and how to evaluate luminaires, you have a much better idea of how a fixture or group of fixtures will work. Know your tools and terminology and you will know your craft.

---

[1] Assuming a perfectly uniform field or beam.

6 ELI THE ICEMAN COMETH

"I sometimes ask myself how it came about that I was the one to develop the theory of relativity. The reason, I think, is that a normal adult never stops to think about problems of space and time. These are things which he has thought about as a child. But my intellectual development was retarded, as a result of which I began to wonder about space and time only when I had already grown up."
- Albert Einstein

If I learned nothing else in college, one lesson that I will never forget is the power of a good mnemonic. A mnemonic is a word or phrase that sparks a memory and helps your recall. I remember having trouble with the phase relationship between the voltage and current in an inductor and a capacitor. Was it an inductor in which the voltage leads the current, or a capacitor in which the current lags the voltage? I never could get it straight. Until, that is, Professor Duesterhoeft taught me a simple mnemonic. "ELI the ICEman."

Life was simpler in high school before I learned about phase relationships. To find the voltage or current you simply used the formula

V(voltage in volts) = I(current in amps) x R(resistance in ohms)

So, if you had a 12 ohm load across a 120 volt circuit, you could easily calculate (assuming you didn't sleep through algebra) that it would draw 10 amps. Of course, lamps are usually rated in watts, not ohms, so in practical terms you would use the formula

P (power in watts) = V x I

Then you could calculate that a 1000W lamp on a 120V circuit will draw about 8.3A.

In high school electronics class, we didn't yet know about inductive or capacitive loads. We lived in blissful ignorance about phase relationships and assumed that all loads were purely resistive. But when we got to college we learned that, in the real world, there is no such thing as a purely resistive load.

Any circuit element has some capacitance or some inductance. If we were dealing with DC, then it would have no consequence. But in the late nineteenth century Nikola Tesla revolutionized power distribution and Thomas Edison's DC power transmission system gave way to AC. In today's power distro, AC is the world we live in.

In order to understand phase relationships, you have to know a little about alternating current (AC). An alternating current varies between its positive peak voltage and its negative peak voltage sixty times each second in a 60 hertz system. Starting at zero, it rises to its peak voltage and then falls through zero volts on the way to its negative peak (see Figure 6-1).

One cycle takes only 1/60th of a second, so it happens very quickly. Since the waveform follows a sine wave, one cycle can be thought of as 360 degrees, as in a circle. If this confuses you, think about it in terms of a turbine generator spinning on its axis converting steam to electricity. In the time it takes to make one revolution, it creates one cycle of ac power. One revolution is 360 degrees. Or you can think of it spinning at 3600 rpm (60 revolutions per second times 60 seconds).

Notice that in the ac waveform below, the peak voltage is actually about 170 volts. A voltmeter measures the average voltage over a period of time. Since the voltage is actually fluctuating very quickly, it can't possibly measure the

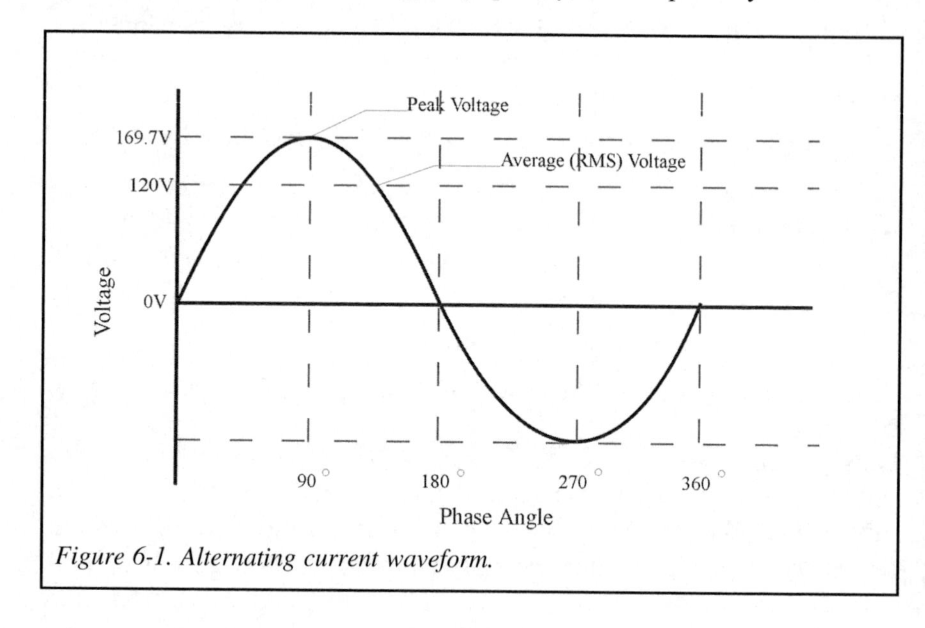

Figure 6-1. Alternating current waveform.

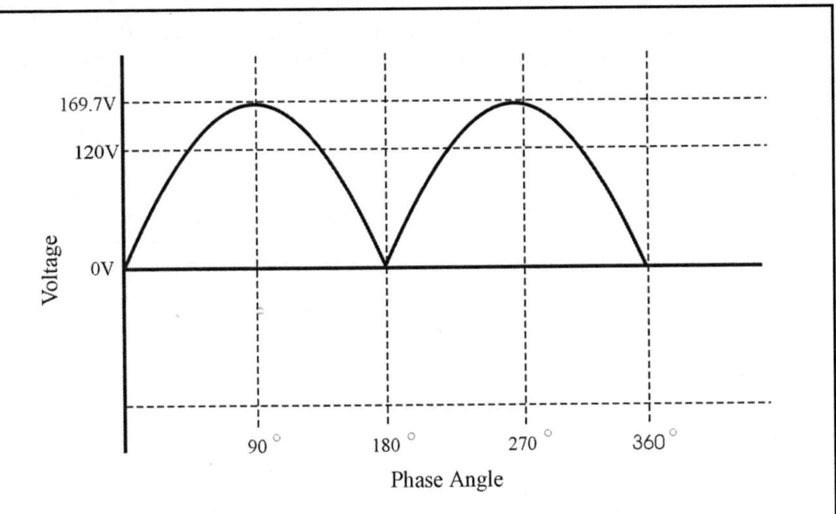

Figure 6.2 - Full Wave Rectification. The second half of the AC cycle is inverted to produce a fully rectified waveform.

instantaneous voltage or your meter would be fluttering like the wings of a hummingbird. Instead, it rectifies, or chops the waveform in half, and inverts the negative half so that both halves are positive voltage (see Figure 6-2). Otherwise the average would be zero volts. This is called full rectification.

If you were to measure the instantaneous voltage at each point along the x-axis and average it at the end of one cycle, you would find that it is equal to .707 times the peak voltage.

$$\mathbf{V_{average} = V_{peak} \times 0.707}$$

That's what your meter reads. The only way you can see all of this actually taking place is with an oscilloscope. But unless you're repairing televisions, most field techs don't pack one. It's usually not necessary.

So who is ELI and where does he come into the picture? I'm glad you asked. Since the current is directly proportional to the voltage (remember V = I x R?), the current is also a sine wave. However, it doesn't always coincide exactly with the voltage. If there is any inductance or capacitance in the load, it will either lag or lead the voltage. In case you are unfamiliar with an inductor or a capacitor, an inductor is simply a coil of wire. You can make an inductor by taking a length of wire and wrapping it around a pencil. A capacitor is made up of two parallel plates of conductive material. In real life, most capacitors are actually two strips of aluminum foil separated by an insulating material and rolled into a cylinder. Both a capacitor and an inductor are energy storage devices. Real life inductors take the form of transformers, ballasts or chokes,

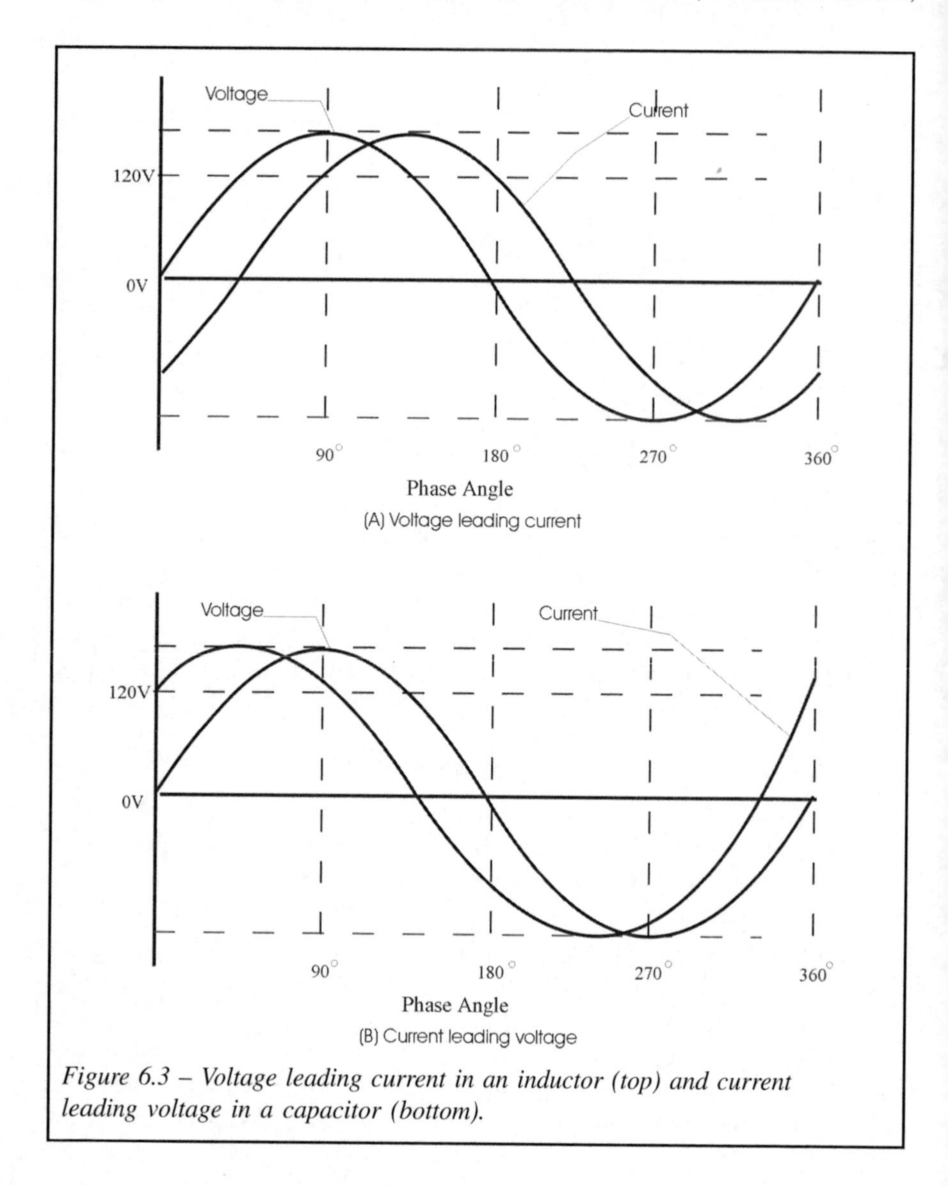

Figure 6.3 – Voltage leading current in an inductor (top) and current leading voltage in a capacitor (bottom).

and some lamp filaments. Capacitors can take the form of cable shields and circuit board traces.

The deal is, there are no purely resistive loads. In real life, every load has elements of resistance, induction, and capacitance, however small. If the total load is more inductive than capacitive, then the voltage leads the current. If the load is more capacitive, then the current leads the voltage. How do I know? Because of ELI the ICEman. Don't ask my why, but in the college of electrical engineering, voltage is sometimes denoted as the letter "E." I think it has to do with the fact that voltage is sometimes referred to as electromotive force, or EMF. Inductance is usually denoted by the letter "L." And, as you would expect, the letters "C" and "I" denote capacitance and current, respectively. Thus, ELI is a mnemonic for E (voltage) leading I (current) in L (an inductor). ICE is a mnemonic for I (current) leading E (voltage) in C (a capacitor).

So what does that have to do with you and me? When the voltage and current are out of phase with each other, the current can rise dramatically. To calculate the current, you have to take into account something called the power factor. The formula is

$$P = V \times I \times \cos(\theta)$$

where θ is the phase angle between the voltage and the current.

COS(θ) is called the power factor. For example, if you have a 1000W inductive load on a 120V circuit and the phase angle is 45°. What's the current? 11.8A. Notice that if the phase angle is 0, then the power factor is 1 [COS(0) = 1] and the current 8.3A. So a phase angle of 45° increases the current 42%! But wait, there's more. The closer the phase angle is to 90°, the higher the current, until it becomes infinite. How would you like to set up a p.d. for that one?!

In short, what happens when the voltage and current are severely out of phase is that more and more current must be generated to produce the same amount of power. For the power company, that translates to bigger generators, cables, steel towers, glass insulators, transformers, switches, connectors, and everything else on the power grid. For the lighting industry, it means bigger and heavier fixtures, connectors, fuses, dimmers, breakers, cable, and everything else on the p.d.

Fortunately, there is a simple solution to the power factor problem. Because of the nature of the power distribution system, loads are usually more inductive than capacitive, especially in industrial areas that have a lot of transformers and motors (read induction!). So the solution is simply to place a capacitor, or bank of capacitors across the line. If you have ever paid much attention to electrical substations you might have noticed a bank of capacitors, usually in large gray steel cans. Or you might have wondered why there was a relatively large capacitor in your discharge fixture. Many fixtures with discharge lamps use a magnetic power supply, which is comprised mainly of the lamp, a starter, and a ballast. The ballast, or choke, is nothing more than an inductor designed to limit the current in the lamp circuit. So some discharge fixtures come standard with a power factor correction capacitor while others offer one as an option. The sole purpose of the cap is to balance the load and bring the voltage and current more in line with each other.

That's the story of Professor Duesterhoeft and Eli the Iceman. Ask me about Dr. Thomas sometime when you have time.

7 DIMMING DEM DOGGONE LIGHTS

"The important thing is not to stop questioning. Curiosity has its own reason for existing. One cannot help but be in awe when he contemplates the mysteries of eternity, of life, of the marvellous structure of reality. It is enough if one tries merely to comprehend a little of this mystery every day. Never lose a holy curiosity."

– Albert Einstein

When I was ten years old, I had a burning curiosity to learn the secret of how radios worked. I was simply amazed that someone sitting miles away in a broadcast studio somewhere could speak into a microphone and his voice could be transmitted without wires across town and then come out of my little radio receiver. The last time I remember using a hammer on electronic apparatus was on this particular summer day in my parent's garage, when the overwhelming desire to learn how this little radio worked overtook me. I carefully took the radio apart looking for clues. What I saw was an intricate puzzle comprised of many electronic components – resistors, transistors, capacitors, and inductors. I was convinced that if I could just have a look inside of one of these components then I could surely solve the mystery of the radio. So I took my father's hammer and began exploring, smashing each component on the concrete floor. What I found was that the epoxy encased transistors didn't reveal their contents very well, and the resistors wound up as a pile of black carbon powder on the floor.

What I learned that day was that casual observation could only take you so far, and after that, you might have to crack a book and spend some time finding answers. The pen, it seems, it truly mightier than the sword (and the hammer). With that in mind, let's take a look at one of the most common electronic devices in the field of entertainment lighting – the dimmer – and see how dimming could possibly change in the future. So for now at least, let's put away our hammers.

Phase Control

In the early days, dimming lights was as simple as reducing the voltage at the load by using a variable resistor or an autotransformer or variac. The resistor method is very inefficient because the resistor dissipates much of the energy in the form of heat. The variac is a much more efficient way to dim a lamp, but it's heavy and bulky, and not very easy to control, especially when there are multiple lights.

Today, the most common method of dimming is called phase controlled dimming. It is so called because it switches the load voltage on and off at a precise phase angle during each cycle of the supply voltage. By doing so it regulates the duty cycle of the load voltage thereby controlling the amount of power consumed by the load. The duty cycle is a ratio comparing the percentage of time during one cycle that something is operating. For instance, if a motor requires one minute of rest for every minute of operation, it has a 50% duty cycle because it should only work 50% of the time.

The preceding paragraph contains a lot of information, especially if you are not very familiar with some of the terms. By way of explanation, you may recall from Chapter 6 (Power Factor Correction) that all AC voltage rises and falls in a sinusoidal waveform 60 times per second. One complete cycle is considered 360° as if it were following the circular motion of an electrical generator, which, of course, it is! (See Figure 7.1)

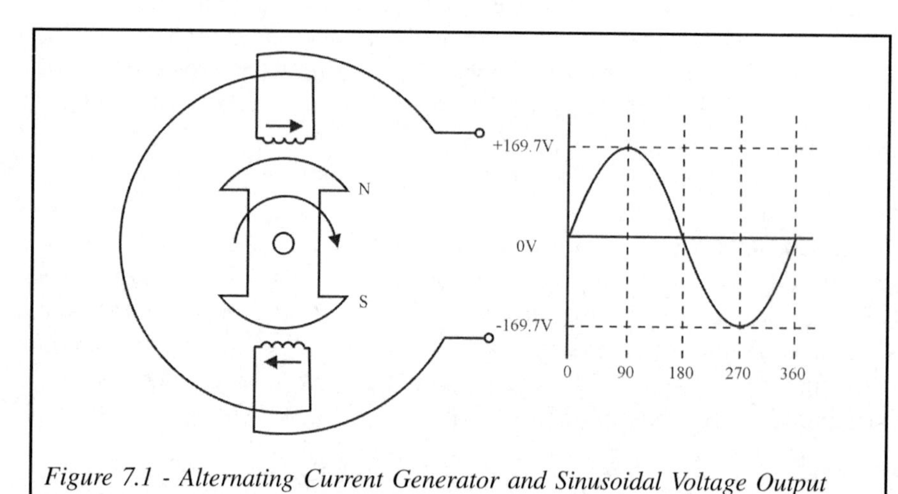

Figure 7.1 - Alternating Current Generator and Sinusoidal Voltage Output Waveform. Each time a pole passes a coil it generates a voltage.

At zero degrees the voltage is zero, and at ninety degrees the voltage is at its positive peak, which, if you happen to live in the U.S. is 170V. We call it 120V because that's the average voltage, or more accurately, the *Root Mean Square* (RMS) for one cycle of the waveform. The RMS voltage can be calculated by finding the square root (Root) of the average (Mean) voltage over one cycle squared, as shown in the set of equations below. But before you let your eyes wander down the page, I'll give you fair warning. If you have an aversion to math, then you're probably not going to like this part. I promise to keep it as brief as possible and then get back to the more palatable squiggles and drawings. Here goes!

$$V_{RMS} = \sqrt{(V^2)}$$

$$V_{RMS} = \sqrt{V_{PEAK}^2 \int_0^{2\pi} \sin^2(\theta)dt}$$

$$V_{RMS} = V_{PEAK}\sqrt{\int_0^{2\pi} \sin^2(\theta)dt}$$

$$V_{RMS} = \frac{V_{PEAK}}{\sqrt{2}}$$

$$V_{RMS} = V_{PEAK} \times .707$$

$$V_{RMS} = 170V \times .707 = 120V$$

If you are familiar with integrals and calculus then you can confirm the information in the equation above. If you are not yet familiar with it or if you are squeamish about math, I encourage you to expand your horizons and learn the 400-year-old art. Otherwise, you'll just have to take my word for it. All that we've done in the five preceding equations was to take the average voltage over one cycle, we squared it, or multiplied it by itself, and then we took the square root of that and multiplied it by the peak voltage. The result is a type of average voltage reading.

Getting back to the sinusoidal voltage waveform, at 180° the voltage falls back to zero again. It's no coincidence, by the way, that the sine of zero degrees is zero, the sine of 90° is one, and the sine of 180° is zero. Do you get the relationship between a sine wave (or voltage waveform) and a circle? The waveform is cyclical through 360° and the peaks, dips, and zero crossing of the voltage correspond with the sine of the angle.

The sine of the phase angle multiplied by the peak voltage gives you the

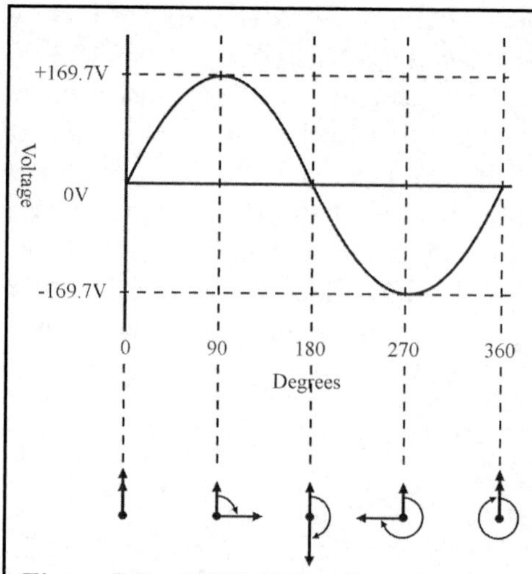

Figure 7.2 – *120VAC Waveform showing peak voltage and 90º increments of phase angle.*

instantaneous voltage.

$$V(\theta) = \sin(\theta) \times V_{peak}$$

where θ = phase angle and V(θ) = instantaneous voltage at phase angle θ

For example, when the phase angle is 90°, the voltage at that moment in time is 170V. At 270º the voltage is -170V.

There it is. We just used trigonometry in a real world application. The next time your kid complains that no one would possibly ever use higher math in real life, ask him to help you design a dimmer without using any math!

I know we've talked a lot about math and a little about actual dimming. But now that we've reviewed AC voltages and phase angles, let's go back to phase controlled dimming. It is so called because it switches the load voltage on and off at a precise phase angle during each cycle of the supply voltage. By doing so it regulates the duty cycle of the load voltage thereby controlling the amount of power consumed by the load.

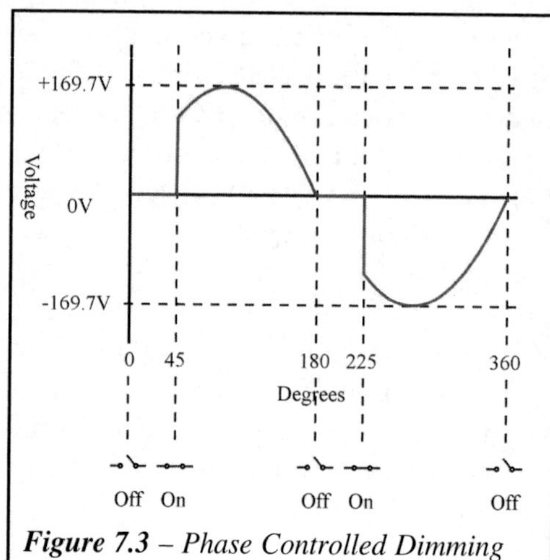

Figure 7.3 – *Phase Controlled Dimming switching "on" at 45º and 225º.*

For example, in Figure 7.3, the voltage is turned on at a phase angle of 45º in the positive half cycle and at 225º in the negative half cycle. The resulting voltage waveform, illustrated in red, produces a lower average voltage than the full cycle, which of course, results in a dimming effect. Note that

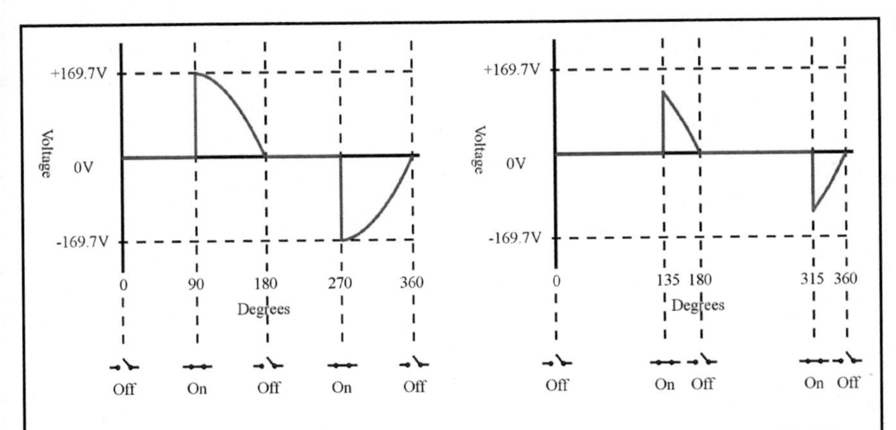

Figure 7.4 (a) – Phase Controlled Dimming switching "on" at 90º and 270º. (b) Switching "on" at 135º and 315º.

the negative half cycle mirrors the positive half cycle; otherwise a DC offset will occur which can wreak havoc on electronic components. Depending on the severity of the offset, it could destroy IC chips, fuses, transformers, printed circuit board traces, and anything else in its path.

Figure 7.4(a) and 7.4(b) above show a progressively lower average voltage as the turn on voltage approaches 180º. Eventually when the phase angle equals 180º then you have a complete blackout.

The illustrations above show a very small time slice. In a 60 Hz electric grid, one cycle occurs every 17 milliseconds. Obviously the controlling switch has to be extremely fast and accurate. Nothing is better suited for speed and accuracy than integrated circuit technology. In this case the most common type of IC chip used for dimming purposes is called a Silicon Controlled Rectifier or SCR for short.

Controlling with Silicon

An SCR is nothing more than a switch, much like a light switch on the wall, with at least two exceptions; it's an electronic switch as opposed to a mechanical switch, and it can only be operated by an electronic signal, not by hand. By applying voltage to one of the three terminals of an SCR, specifically the gate, it allows current to pass through the other two terminals (anode and cathode).

How does it do that? Well, you can get a good look inside if you take a

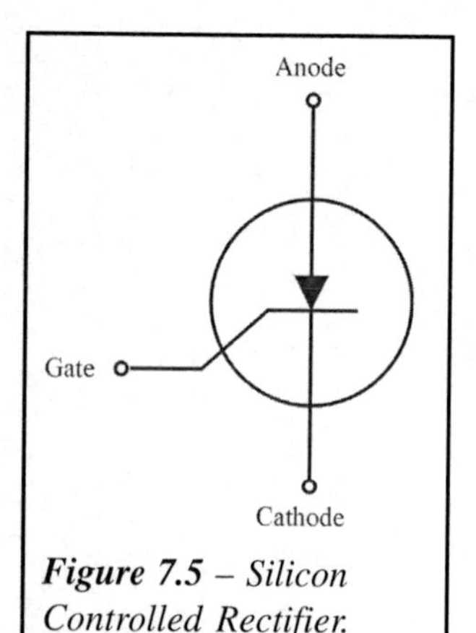

Figure 7.5 *– Silicon Controlled Rectifier.*

hammer and… No, wait. I already tried that and I can tell you, it doesn't work. The working part of an SCR is a rather small junction of different types of silicon encased in an epoxy package like a transistor. The epoxy just doesn't yield its secrets very well. Suffice it to say that it's a type of transistor that deals well with high voltage and current.

If you remember the diagram above showing how the voltage is turned on and off at specific phase angles, then you can understand how a simple switch can dim a lighting load. It's just a matter of sending the proper signal to the gate at the proper time. The proper signal is a small voltage applied to the gate, at least as high as the threshold voltage, to turn on the switch. When the switch is on, the SCR completes the circuit between the line voltage and the load. Figure 7.6, below, illustrates how the load voltage is turned on and off when the control voltage goes from low to high. Typically the turn on voltage is around 5Vdc.

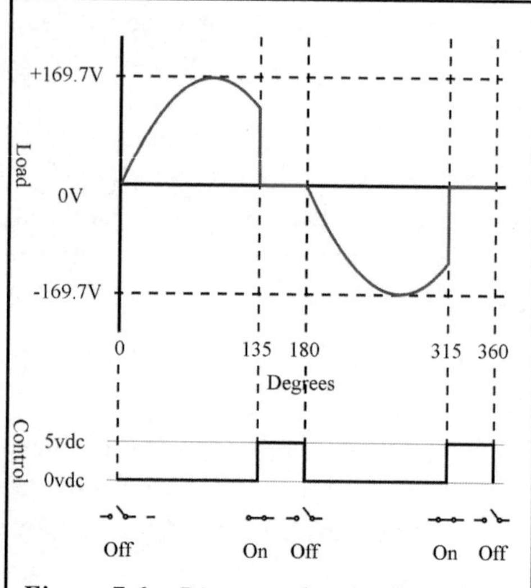

Figure 7.6 *– Diagram showing how the control voltage turns the load voltage on and off.*

If you're paying close attention and you know something about SCR's, then no doubt you noticed that the diagram shows full-wave control, while an SCR is a directional beast. That means that an SCR can conduct only in one direction, or for one half cycle of the voltage waveform. What you're seeing in the diagram actually requires two SCR's hooked up back-to-back, or in parallel-inverted fashion so that one of them is oriented in one direction and the other in the opposite direction. One SCR conducts during the positive half-cycle and the other in the

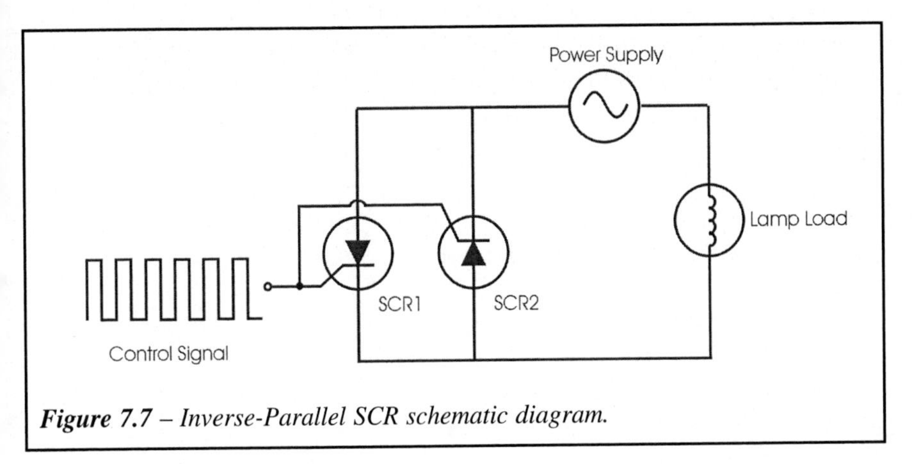

***Figure** 7.7 – Inverse-Parallel SCR schematic diagram.*

negative half-cycle. Together, the two of them produce the entire waveform. This scheme has at least one great benefit. While one SCR is conducting, the other is cooling. The 50% duty cycle allows the components to last far longer than a triac in the same circuit. A triac is functionally similar to an SCR, but it is bi-directional, allowing it to conduct in both directions during the entire waveform. The drawback to using unidirectional components is that the chip count is higher and costlier.

That's all it takes, in theory, to dim a lighting load. You might be saying to yourself, "Self, why are dimming racks so big and heavy if all they have in them are a couple of SCR's and control circuitry?" If you've ever hauled a dimmer rack up a ramp then you know what I'm talking about. Ah, the devil is in the details. There are funny things that happen when you suddenly turn on the voltage midway through the waveform. When the voltage goes from nothing to something in a short time, the current makes a massive attempt to keep up. It's something like opening all the floodgates at Hoover Dam instantaneously. Everything downstream gets a massive surge. The streams overflow their banks, the thousand-year flood plane goes underwater, and everyone's insurance premium goes up. In electrical terms, a surge makes conduit jump, circuits are stressed, and lamp filaments get a jolt. Surely there's a better way.

Choking the Current

The better way is to choke the current, or limit the current rise by inserting an inductor in series with the load. The inductor is nothing more than a coil of wire that opposes a change in current by creating a magnetic field in the opposite direction of the current flow. The bigger the current change, the stronger the magnetic field, thus the stronger the choking action. Inserting an iron core in the center of the coil strengthens the magnetism and makes a more effective choke. That's the good part about iron core chokes. The bad part is that iron and copper have a strong attraction to the center of the earth. In other words, they're heavy. That's why you should work really hard to become a briefcase programmer and leave the load-ins and outs to the professionals.

The choke limits the rise time of the load current, which is one of the most important aspects of a dimmer. The longer the rise time, the easier it is on the entire system, including transformers, cables, lamps, and nerves. Conversely, a system with a short rise time produces current spikes that can work transformers very hard, causing them to overheat and shorten their lives.

Often times, the issue arises whether or not it is acceptable to power automated lighting from a dimmer rack. To do so almost certainly invites trouble because of the nature of the dimming circuit. When the dimming circuit is not fully on it alters the purity of the sine wave and introduces harmonics that can damage circuit components. Look back at figure 7.6 and notice how the leading edge of the waveform creates a sharp rise in voltage and sharp "edges" on the waveform. It's clearly not a pure sine wave.

Any type of periodic waveform, or a waveform that repeats itself, can be broken down into a series of sine waves with various amplitudes and multiples of the original frequency, or harmonics. For example, it's possible to recreate the distinct sound of your voice by using a series of sine waves at differing volumes and frequencies. I didn't say it was easy, but by using a mathematically technique called Fourier analysis each harmonic can be calculated.

In a dimmed circuit such as the one shown in figure 7.6, the strongest harmonic is the third multiple of the original frequency (60Hz in North America, 50Hz almost everywhere else). What happens is that as the circuit is dimmed, the third harmonic generates a very high current, which can overload the circuit and damage sensitive components like cables, PC boards, IC chips, transformers, chokes, and anything else in the path of the current. But you recall that by adding a choke to the dimming circuit it reduces the initial current surge. Nonetheless, it still exists, just to a lesser degree.

Granted, as long as the control signal is holding the circuit at full on, such as with a parked channel, the dimmer output should be a pure sine wave, or very close to it. But the normal state of the SCR is off, so if there is any glitch or voltage drop, then the sine wave loses its purity. Lightning strike? Power surge? Someone trips over the feed? All asking for trouble. Besides, it's much more costly to use a parked dimming channel than to use a feed from the distro panel.

Reverse Phase Control

Conventional dimming uses forward phase control techniques, which we discussed in the preceding paragraphs. Reverse phase control dimming is similar except that instead of turning the voltage on during the sine wave, it turns the voltage off at a certain phase angle. It is accomplished by using a type of IC chip called an insulated gate bipolar transistor, or IGBT, instead of SCR's. An IGBT is a high current switching device that has the ability to switch on or off any time during the voltage cycle, not only at the zero crossing. It sounds simple enough, you say, but what are the advantages? I'm glad you asked.

Breaking the Choke Hold

First of all, it doesn't use a choke. It doesn't require one. When you simply cut off the voltage mid-way during the voltage cycle, it doesn't produce a current spike like it does when you turn on the voltage during the cycle. In simple terms, when you go from zero volts to 50 or 100 volts or more, as it does in a forward phase control dimming circuit, the current tries to catch up very quickly and "overshoots" the steady-state current. It produces a very large current for a short period of time. On the other hand, when you go from 50 or 100 volts or more to zero volts as in the reverse phase control scheme, the current simply drops to zero as the circuit discharges and allows it to fall.

No choke means less weight, less heat, and more efficiency.

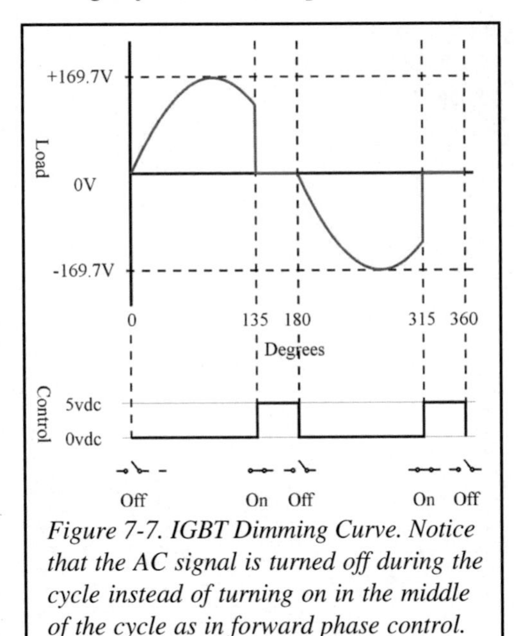

Figure 7-7. IGBT Dimming Curve. Notice that the AC signal is turned off during the cycle instead of turning on in the middle of the cycle as in forward phase control.

In short, smaller, lighter, better. The choke is one of the heaviest, if not *the* heaviest component in most good quality dimmers. It's also responsible for the biggest inefficiencies of conventional dimming. A typical choke, which is nothing more than a coil of wire wrapped around an iron core, drops a few volts across its windings. So what's a few volts between friends? In a 20A circuit it's about 20 watts per volt. That's lost power. Any devotee of Newtonian physics will tell you that energy cannot be created or destroyed. The energy simply turns from electrical energy to heat energy. So by giving up the choke, you save on electricity and air conditioning bills.

Stoopid Dimming Tricks

One manufacturer of an IGBT dimming system, Entertainment Technology, has patented a way of controlling troubling harmonics that cause transformer and wiring inefficiencies. By using both forward and reverse phase control in the same system, harmonics are produced that combine and cancel each other out in the neutral circuit. This method helps extend the life of feeder transformers and eases wear on electrical systems in general.

To read more about IGBT dimming you can visit the web sites of two companies who manufacture IGBT dimmers, IES and Entertainment Technology (Genlyte-Thomas Group) at www.ies.nl and www.rosco-et.com respectively.

8 REAL LIGHTING TECHS

"I do the best I know how, the very best I can; and I mean to keep on doing it to the end. If the end brings me out all right, what is said against me will not amount to anything. If the end brings me out wrong, ten angels swearing I was right would make no difference."
– Abraham Lincoln

Bill McCarty was a man who stood tall among lighting techs, always reliable and never hesitating to live life. In 1991 I sent him on the road as the moving light tech on the Dire Straits *One Every Street* world tour. He brought with him a keen mind for electronics technology, an eye for detail, and the largest hospital roadcase I had ever seen, stuffed with every conceivable spare part he might ever need, down to the last fastener. Though he was unproven on the road at the time, he came off the road with the admiration and respect of everyone he worked with. Everyone I spoke to about him at the time boasted of his hard work and his dependability. Whenever he was sent on a job, everyone breathed a small sigh of relief because they knew they could rely on him to keep everything working. He was fastidious in his duties and he made notes with an incredible amount of detail. Sometimes he would drive me crazy with his persistence and detail, with long phone calls about engineering problems and requests to refill his magic war chest. But I always knew it was his way of doing his job as best he could. His bus mates came to know him as the hard charging Texan with the Aussie bush hat. At load-out, he would button up the side of the hat as if he were leading a cavalry charge. They also knew him for his "cowboy killers," the bottomless stash of Marlboro cigarettes in the red box that were so difficult to find in Europe. Yet Bill always had them. In the end, they proved tougher than the man and probably contributed to his early demise on the first day of October 2000. Bill had a heart attack and checked out of this mortal coil in the waning hours of the day while he was still in his early forties.

Here are some of the things I learned from Bill about being the kind of road tech or bench tech that keeps getting called back and that crews are happy to work with.

Bill McCarty – stood tall among lighting techs.

Be Prepared

A little preparation goes a long way and a lot of preparation gets you noticed. You can't plan for every contingency, but you should have all the basics covered and then some. Being prepared means lining up as many replacement parts ahead of time as you possibly can. And if that means taking along a big hospital case, then so be it. If truck space is limited, then at least make sure yours is the biggest hospital case on the entire tour! Carry your spares proudly and don't be ashamed if you have more spares than a competing brand. It's not about how frequently you need spares, but how infrequently you don't have them. It's about how often all your lights are up and running.

Work Hard

Strive to be the hardest worker on your crew. Even if it's not in your job description, be the one who pushes the most roadcases, lifts the most boxes, coils the most cable, packs and unpacks the most instruments, tightens the most bolts, and fixes the most problems. Be the first one ready to go and the last one ready to leave. And do it a smile on your face and a song in your heart.

Study Your Craft

Spend enough time learning your craft so that you know it backwards and forwards. Learn it so well that people come to you for answers and to settle bets. Be the one that everyone knows they can count on for reliable information, knowledge and expertise. Then act as if you're just an average lighting Joe.

Share Your Good Fortune

When fortune smiles on you, share it with those around you. Buy your crew a round of beer every now and then and if you insist on smoking share your cigarettes with them. Share your knowledge as if you gain more by giving more.

Have a Good Attitude

Be positive. Make people like you. Shrug off your problems and bring a fresh attitude to work every day. Every now and again thank your crewmates and the people you work with. Be sincere about expressing your appreciation and never be afraid to look them in the eye, shake their hands, pat them on the back and give a few words of thanks. Make them wonder what you're really up to.

Enjoy Life

Have fun. Soak it up while you can. Revel in the good times and remember them when things are not going well. Learn to appreciate some of the finer things in life. Things like good friends, a fine stereo system, and an old pickup truck.

Adios, Bill.

9 THE INVERSE SQUARE LAW

"Bend me shape me, anyway you want me,
You've got the power to turn on the light."
- The American Breed

Why do lights lose intensity the farther they project? You can't just take a projector and throw an image on a building from across the street and expect it to read as if it were projecting a couple of feet. What happens to light as it travels through space? Why does it fade and where does it go? It can't just disappear. There must be an explanation for this phenomenon.

It's been said in this book before and it will be said again. Light is energy and energy can neither be created nor destroyed. Like the bumper sticker says, it's not just a good idea, it's the law. So we can't lose light, but we can bend it, shape it, any way we want it. A diverging beam of light spreads out and becomes weaker and weaker until it's undetectable. The inverse square law describes how the illumination of a surface falls off exponentially in relation to the throw distance.

$$\text{Illumination} = \frac{\text{Luminous Intensity}}{\text{distance}^2}$$

What exactly does that mean? The relationship is easy to understand if you think in terms of the area the light covers. The angle of projection and the throw distance determines the size of the spot produced by the beam.

Remember in high school trigonometry class when you were given one angle and one side and you were asked to solve the triangle? This is the same thing, except the Bee Gees aren't dominating the charts, and I haven't seen any 8-track tape decks and leisure suits since then.

For a fixed beam angle and a known projection distance, you can figure out the size of the spot a luminaire will produce. The key is to bisect the beam and create a right triangle as illustrated below.

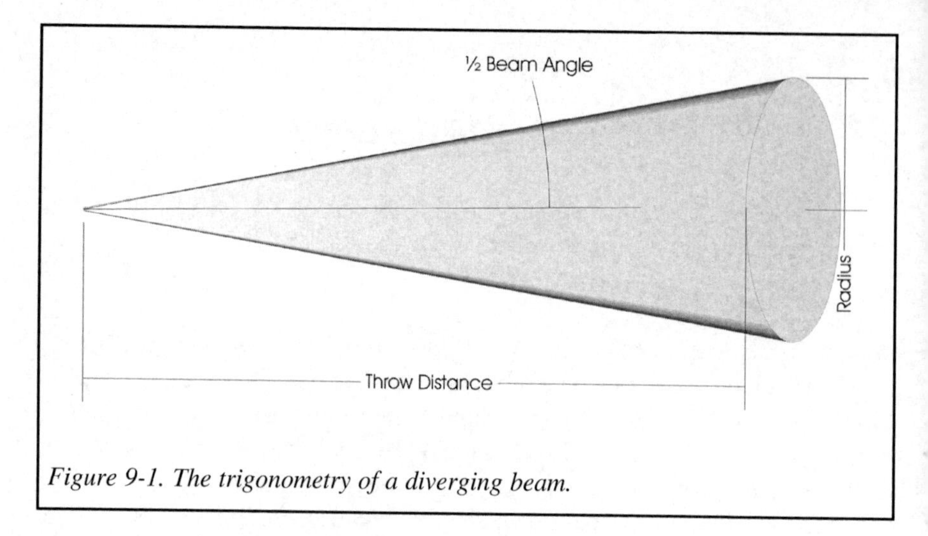

Figure 9-1. The trigonometry of a diverging beam.

$$\theta = \frac{1}{2}\text{Beam Angle}$$

$$\text{distance} = \text{projection distance}$$

$$\text{radius} = \frac{1}{2}\ \text{Beam Diameter}$$

In case it's been as long for you as it has for me, I'll give you the trigonometric equation to solve for the radius if you know the projection distance and the beam angle.

$$\text{radius} = \text{distance} \times \tan\theta$$

Once you know the radius of the spot, you can calculate the area the light covers.

$$\text{Area} = \pi \times \textit{radius}^2$$

To borrow from Frank Zappa, here is the crux of the biscuit. When the light from a luminaire strikes a surface, it is distributed over the area of the spot. Since the area is proportional to the square of the radius, whenever the radius increases then the area of coverage increases exponentially. And the radius increases in direct proportion to the projection distance. So for a longer throw, the same amount of light has to cover exponentially more surface area. Therefore, the illumination decreases exponentially.

Now wasn't that at least as fun as your high school prom?

Getting Around the Law

There's no getting around the inverse square law. But you can change selected parameters to achieve your desired result.

If you narrow the beam angle to keep the size of the spot the same while you increase the projection distance, then guess what? Since the light is spread over the same area then the surface is illuminated exactly the same. Longer projection distance, more narrow beam, same illumination. In real life there are certain losses associated with longer projection distances. Fog, smoke, dust, and pollution scatter the beam and introduce some losses. In a perfect vacuum, like catching light in a bottle, there are no losses.

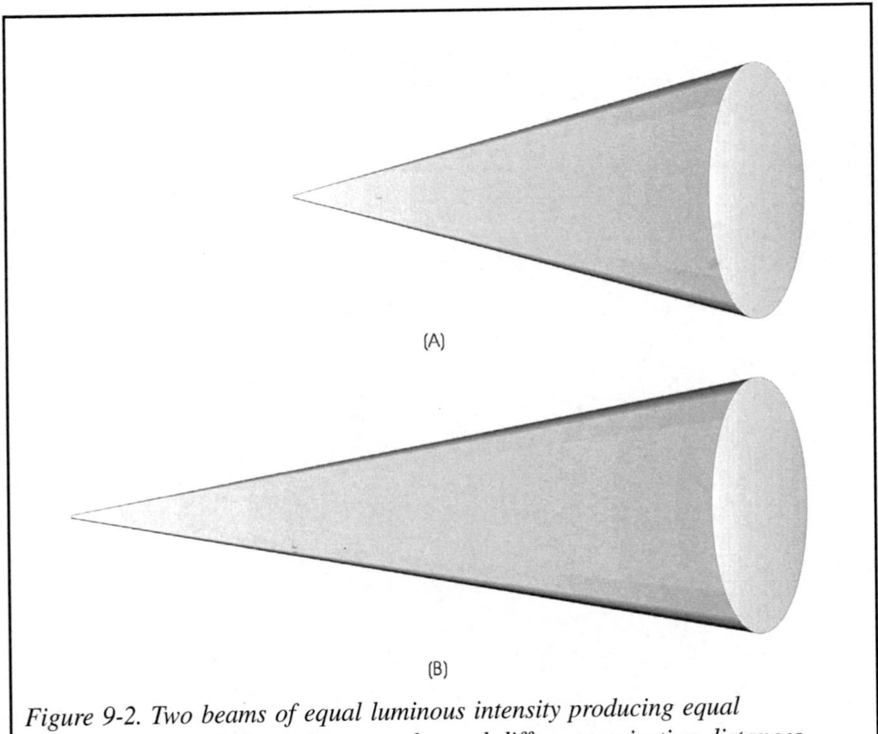

Figure 9-2. Two beams of equal luminous intensity producing equal illumination with different beam angles and different projection distances.

In practice, a narrow beam angle requires bigger lenses and a longer optical train. A very long throw fixture is often several feet long, something like a followspot. In fact, a followspot is a very long throw fixture designed to produce an intense spot on an area approximately the size of a person.

Photometrics

Some manufacturers give you photometric data in the form of the beam angle and the luminous intensity in candelas. With those two pieces of information, you should be able to use the above formulas to calculate the size of the beam and the illumination for a given projection distance.

The Inverse of the Inverse Square Law

The inverse square law applies to a diverging beam. What if the beam was converging instead? If you think in terms of the area of the spot and what happens with a converging beam, then you can guess how it would work.

For a converging beam, the illumination would increase with the projection distance. Do you recognize the illustration as a magnifying glass? It's also the same principle that makes satellite dishes work.

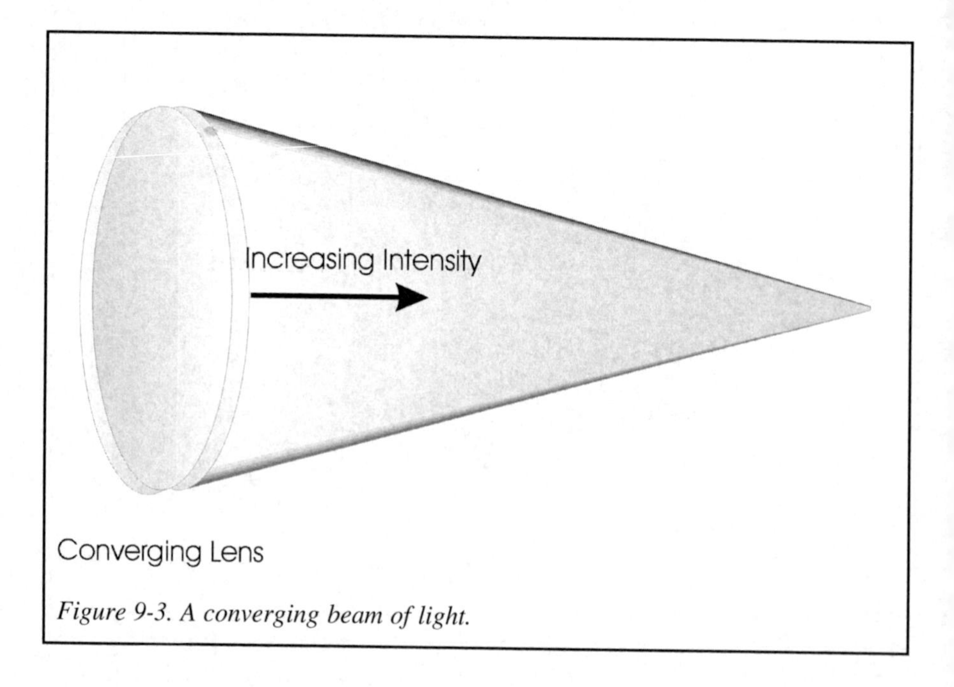

Figure 9-3. A converging beam of light.

The alternative to either a diverging beam or a converging beam is a coherent light, or a laser beam. A laser beam, in principal, neither diverges nor converges.

Intuition tells us that the longer the projection distance, the weaker the illumination. But if you think in terms of a variable beam angle, as in a zoom ellipsoidal fixture, you can use the same principle to make your lighting design work for you. Spend some quality time with your Maglight playing with the beam angle and you'll see what I mean.

10 ACHROMATIC LENSES

"Knowledge speaks, but wisdom listens."
– Jimi Hendrix

Have you ever looked at a lighting fixture spec and wondered what an achromatic lens is? A friend once e-mailed to me a link about the problem of chromatic aberration (http://www.utmem.edu/~thjones/hist/c5.htm) in response to the many questions he was receiving about achromatic lenses. The web page tells an interesting story about the development of the microscope and how the achromatic lens was developed. I'll try not to plagiarize the story and I'll let you visit the site and read it for yourself. It makes for very interesting reading, especially since the proliferation of dichroic gobos and the increased importance of projections as opposed to aerial beams in entertainment lighting. Instead, I'd like to talk about the principle of the achromatic lens – how it works and why it's important.

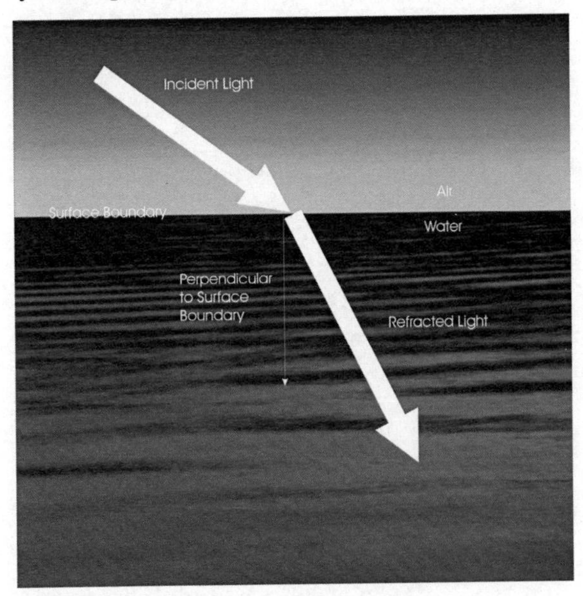

Figure 10.1 - Light Refracting in Water.

Refraction

Students of physics can rattle off the speed of light in a flash, but do you know that the famous constant only pertains to light in a vacuum? The speed, and possibly the direction of light changes when it travels through any substance other than a vacuum. Light travels slower through water than it does through air – not that you would notice, except for one thing. When it passes from one medium to another with a different speed, it bends or "refracts" in the direction perpendicular to the interface boundary. That's why a straight object appears to bend when it's sticking out of the water.

Scientists like to quantify, or assign numbers to anything and everything, sticklers that they are. So they measure how much a substance changes the speed of light relative to a vacuum and they call that the index of refraction. Thus, the index of refraction for any substance is the ratio of the velocity of light in a vacuum to its velocity in the substance.

$$\text{Index of Refraction} = \frac{\text{Speed of light in a vacuum}}{\text{Speed of light in a substance}}$$

By looking at a table of the index of refraction for different materials you can see how much the material affects light.

You might be asking yourself, "Self, how does all this affect me, Al 'Lighting Designer' Franken?" Refraction plays an important role in the quality of light projected by your tools of the trade. Most every luminaire contains an optical system with at least one or more lenses that obey the laws of physics, including refraction and something called dispersion.

Substance	Index	Substance	Index
Vacuum	1.0	Diamond	2.417
Air	1.000277	Crown Glass	1.50-1.62
Water	1.333	Flint Glass	1.57-1.75

Table 10-1. Index of Refraction for Various Materials

Dispersion

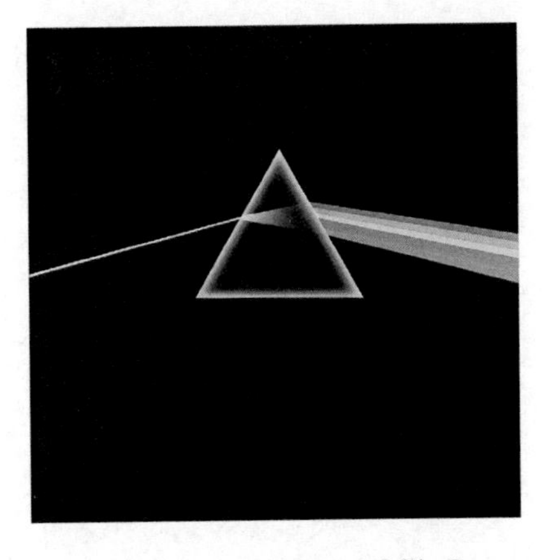

Up until now we have made no reference to the wavelength of the light involved in refraction. It turns out that the amount of refraction varies by wavelength so that different wavelengths, or colors, refract differently by the same material. This is called chromatic dispersion. White light that is refracted tends to disperse into its component colors. Remember Pink Floyd's *Dark Side of the Moon* album cover? It illustrates a prime example of chromatic dispersion – a prism. Okay, students of Sir Isaac Newton may argue that his publication of *Opticks* in 1704 was more far-reaching and important than Pink Floyd. But then I never saw one of his light shows.

Aberration

Chromatic dispersion is important to those of us in the entertainment lighting field because it can produce distortion in a lens. The glass in a lens refracts blue light differently than it does red light, consequently, the focal point is slightly different for each wavelength. The resulting image is difficult to focus and it may produce a colorful outer edge where none is intended. This is called a chromatic aberration. It makes your gobos and projections difficult to focus and it causes a white spotlight to have a chromatic halo.

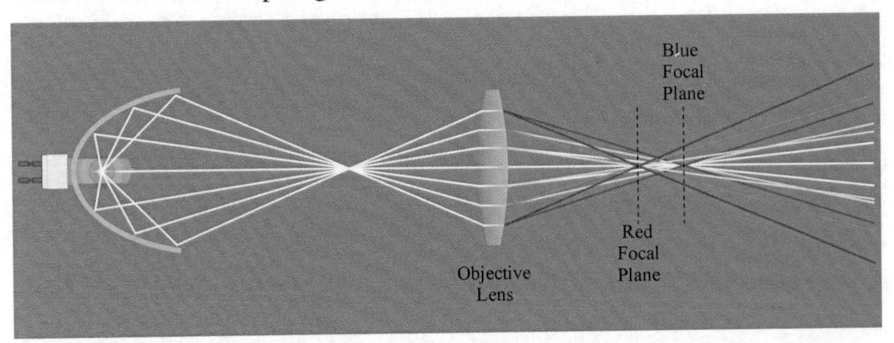

Figure 10.3 - Chromatic Aberration. This illustration shows how the focal point varies for different wavelengths after experiencing chromatic aberration.

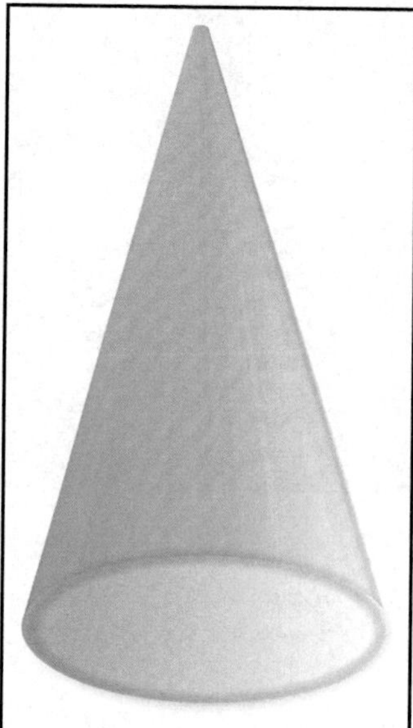

Figure 10-4. The telltale red ring around the spot indicates the absence of an achromatic lens.

Achromatic Lenses

The fix for this problem is the subject of the previously mentioned link to the story of the development of the achromatic lens. A very clever person reasoned that if a lens dispersed the components of white light, then a concave lens with a higher index of refraction could put them back together again. By combining a lens made of crown glass with a concave lens made of flint glass, which has a higher index of refraction than crown glass, the focal lengths of each wavelength are refracted in such a way as to cancel out. Thus, the focal distance is the same for each color in the spectrum. The resulting projection produces images that are easier to focus and have reduced chromatic aberrations (see figure 10-5).

Achromatic lenses are made by cementing a crown glass lens to a concave lens made of flint glass. As one would expect, they cost more than a single lens and they are generally found in better quality fixtures. As more and more luminaires are offering glass gobos with high resolution etched dichroic patterns and indexing capability, the imaging quality is becoming more and more important for good quality projections.

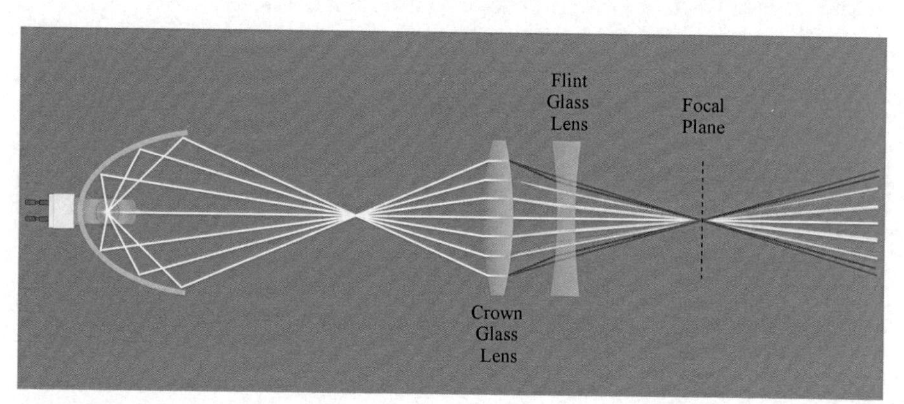

Figure 10-5. Achromatic Doublet Coupling Crown Glass and Flint Glass.

The term "achromatic" literally means without hue or color. An achromatic lens can do its job with little or no color separation. They produce sharper, clearer images, and they can make a hundred dollar gobo look like a million bucks.

11 MAGNETIC CIRCUIT BREAKERS

"All truths are easy to understand once they are discovered; the point is to discover them."
- Galileo, the first celebrity to go by only one name.

I'll never forget how I learned about magnetic circuit breakers. It was at a trade show in Italy where we were introducing a new product called Dataflash. We set up a huge display with 264 fixtures. It was the largest computer-controlled dimmable strobe system ever seen at the time. I was almost giddy with excitement in anticipation of witnessing it in action. But no sooner than the first flashes began, circuit breakers began tripping like popcorn kernels in an inferno. We were dumbfounded. We had tested and re-tested the fixtures in the shop before we left and never did we have that problem. What could be causing the circuit breakers to trip?

It turns out that the breaker panel we rented was full of magnetic circuit breakers. They responded much faster than the thermal circuit breakers that we were accustomed to, and they would not tolerate the large, albeit short, current demand. After wrestling with the problem for hours on end, the only solution we could find was to manually reset the breakers as fast as possible. So for four straight days during the show, we took turns behind a curtain flipping magnetic circuit breakers as fast as we could. I spent hours behind the curtain, and I had lots of time to think about magnetic circuit breakers. Why anyone would want magnetic circuit breakers as opposed to "normal" thermal circuit breakers?

Common household circuit breakers that you find in most houses in the U.S. are thermal circuit breakers. They are relatively inexpensive and they can be found in many hardware stores and electrical supply houses. They work on the principle of heat expansion and contraction.

Getting Hot and Bothered

When electricity flows through a wire the current and resistance causes the copper to heat up. My high school electronics teacher, Harry Hamilton (we called him Harry) had a unique way of teaching. He taught us about how current flowing through a resistor produces heat. He likened it to a narrow hallway with pretty girls on one end and young men on the other. The guys would run down the hall trying to get to the girls, bumping into each other, getting all hot and bothered. In an electrical circuit, as the electrical charges travel down a conductor with a characteristic resistance (in the real world all conductors have some resistance at room temperature), they literally bump into each other and the friction produces heat. The amount of heat that it produces is exponentially proportional to the amount of current (I) and directly proportional to the amount of resistance in the circuit. The heat is exactly equal to the power dissipated in the circuit, or I^2R, because energy (or power) can neither be created nor destroyed. It has to go somewhere. And that somewhere is in the heat that radiates from the components in the circuit. That's why the new super fast computers need at least one fan on the CPU. Mine has three fans in it. It uses more current and thus produces more heat. But that was Harry's way of helping us visualize the principal of I^2R causing heat.

In a thermal circuit breaker the trigger mechanism has a bi-metallic strip in series with the circuit. As the name implies, it operates by the principle of heat expansion. Most objects expand when they heat up. This circuit breaker is made of two dissimilar metals that have different coefficients of expansion. The coefficient of expansion tells you how much it expands for a given increase in temperature. When the current reaches a predetermined point, it heats the bi-metallic strip. Since each type of metal expands at a different rate the heat causes a deflection of the bi-metallic strip, which opens the circuit and stops the flow of electricity.

Magnetic circuit breakers, on the other hand, operate on the principal of magnetic flux. When alternating current flows through a wire, it develops a magnetic flux around the wire. The lines of flux flow in the direction that the fingers of your right hand would wrap if your thumb pointed in the direction of the current flow. The intensity of the magnetic flux is proportional to the amount of current. The greater the current, the stronger the magnetic flux. When the wire is wrapped around a cylinder to form a coil, the center of the coil develops a strong magnetic flux when current flows through it. To make it even stronger, you can insert an iron core. The iron increases the inductance and the magnetic flux. If the iron core is allowed to float freely in the coil, it will move in the direction of the magnetic flux. That's how you build a solenoid.

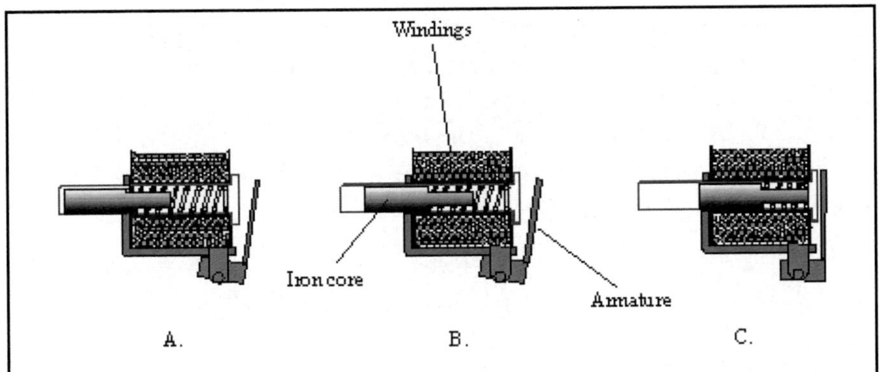

Figure 11.1 - Magnetic Circuit Breaker. A. Open position with unenergized coil. B. Open position with energized coil. C. Contacts closed and coil energized.

Tripping with Magnetism

A magnetic circuit breaker utilizes the flux developed by the current flowing in the circuit. The trigger mechanism has a solenoid in series with the circuit. The solenoid, as we said, is nothing more than a coil of wire wrapped around and iron core. As the current increases, so does the magnetic flux in the coil. The magnetism attracts and pulls an armature, which trips and interrupts the circuit.

Magnetic circuit breakers are less common and more expensive than thermal circuit breakers. So why would anyone want to use them?

For several reasons.

First of all, they are faster than thermal circuit breakers. A magnetic circuit breaker can respond to high current in as little as .01 seconds. By contrast, a thermal breaker takes time to heat up before it trips, usually about .04 or .05 seconds. That explains why I had to spend so much time resetting those magnetic breakers for the strobe system. The breakers were dutifully doing their job, and very quickly I might add. That's great if you want to protect expensive and sensitive electronic equipment. Not so great if you're firing strobes.

Secondly, magnetic breakers will always carry their fully rated current regardless of the ambient temperature. On the other hand, thermal breakers have to be de-rated if they are used in high ambient temperatures because the thermal sensing element has less overhead. If you have a dimmer rack full of thermal breakers and you're doing an outdoor show in Phoenix in the mid-day sun, you could be asking for trouble. Can you say nuisance tripping?

Thirdly, magnetic circuit breakers can be reset immediately. Thermal breakers require a cooling off period after tripping.

Thermal circuit breakers have their place, as do magnetic breakers. Whenever I see a spec that has magnetic circuit breakers, usually on dimmer specs, I think about my experience in Italy. That certainly wasn't the place for them.

12 STEP THIS WAY

"These are the days of miracle and wonder ..." – Paul Simon and Forere Motlobeloa from the song 'The Boy in the Bubble'

In 1986 Paul Simon won a Grammy for Album of the Year with *Graceland*, an explosion at the Chernobyl nuclear power plant sent a large radiation cloud over much of Europe, and the space shuttle Challenger exploded after launching from Cape Canaveral. And in the small town of Castel Goffredo, not far from Milan, Coemar was shipping one of the first automated moving lights that you could take home with you if you ponied up a few million Lira. It was called the Robot and it used an HTI 250 lamp with a Mark 350 power supply. It also had Airtronics servomotors for pan, tilt, color, and gobo selection.

Servo Motors and Pencil Shavings

A servomotor is a motor with a feedback loop and a sensing circuit. The feedback loop tells the electronics the exact position of the shaft at all times. It's a clever way of positioning things like the steering on radio-controlled cars and the pan and tilt on a moving light. And the very thing that makes it useful for precision positioning also makes it vulnerable to failure. The feedback loop has a potentiometer (remember the volume control on your transistor radio? That's a potentiometer) geared to the motor shaft. The position of the motor shaft controls the position of the potentiometer through the gear set, which in turn generates a voltage proportional to the radial position of the shaft. The voltage is fed to a comparator circuit, which compares it to the control voltage. If there is a difference between the two then it generates a voltage that makes the shaft of the motor turn until the feedback voltage and the control voltage are the same. A positive voltage differential might make the shaft turn one direction while a negative voltage differential makes it turn the opposite direction.

In the Airtronics servos, the gears were made of plastic. Not the new space-age plastic that you find in automated lighting today, but easily breakable plastic. The same kind that they used to use in those transistor radios. If you dropped them hard enough they would break into enough pieces that you would be finding parts for days. The plastic servo gears were the same. If they encountered enough resistance they would simply break. You could break the servo by holding the mirror and preventing it from moving when the servo was engaged. The gears would either strip or break.

If the gears didn't break, then eventually the potentiometer would wear out. A potentiometer has a wiper arm with a contactor that rotates along a resistive path to vary the resistance in the circuit. The contactor is made of carbon and it has a limited life. After several hours of use the contactor tends to crumble into powder much like a pencil lead after heavy use. The powder interferes with the contactor and changes the resistance of the potentiometer. It's the same problem that causes static in the volume control of older analog radios. The problem is exacerbated in moving lights when the servo is panned and tilted at a high rate of speed for lots of repetitions. The faster the movements, the quicker the failures occurred.

Stepper Motors and Sensors

Shortly after the Coemar Robot, Clay Paky started shipping the Golden Scan. It was more advanced and used stepper motors instead of servomotors. They were ultimately more reliable because they lacked the two things that caused the problems in the servos – they had no gears and no feedback. Instead, the shaft is inductively coupled with no hardware connecting the rotor and the stator. When a coil of wire on the stator is energized – when current is passed through it – it creates a magnetic field that attracts an oppositely charged magnet on the rotor. Consequently, you can grab hold of a spinning stepper motor and the worst thing that will happen is that it will lose its position. That's the reason that most moving lights now use sensors – either optical or magnetic – to sense the position of the object under control of the stepper motor. There are no gears in the motor but they also have no fixed reference point. They have to rely on sensors to relay to the processor the position of the shaft. That's accomplished by an initialization procedure. During the initialization procedure (on startup when you hear all the clattering), the stepper motors are being aligned in their home positions. Once they are aligned, the processor knows that they are in the home position. In lieu of the feedback loop, the microprocessor then keeps track of how many steps forward or backward it has taken so it always knows the exact angular position of the shaft.

Stepper motors are inherently not as smooth as an AC or DC motor. As the name implies, they move in steps, albeit small ones. Just about every moving light specification these days touts microstepping as a feature, as if it's a new idea unique to that individual fixture. That's something akin to bragging that the beam *actually moves!* Get over it already. I think the professional lighting community is so well informed today that we automatically assume that every fixture uses microstepping and if it doesn't it will be viewed with a jaundiced eye!

So we know that if a moving light is going to have a prayer of moving nice and smoothly that it should be microstepped. But what exactly is microstepping and how does it work? We'll examine a stepper motor moving in full steps, half steps, and microsteps.

One Small Step

All stepper motors have in common a stator and a rotor. The stator has several pole pieces arranged in a circle around the rotor and shaft and each pole piece has a winding of copper wire. The windings are arranged in polar opposite pairs on opposite sides of the motor. When they are energized, one coil produces a magnetic field in one direction, say North, while the coil on the opposite side of the stator produces a magnetic field in the opposite direction - South. The rotor has several permanent magnets or in the case of certain types of stepper motors called variable reluctance motors, they have a cylindrical core made of magnetic material with toothed cogs cut into it. When a pair of pole pieces on the stator is energized, the teeth are magnetically attracted to them and move to align themselves according to the proximity of the energized pole pieces.

Stepper motors rely on fairly sophisticated control systems (a.k.a. microprocessors) to tell the motor precisely when to step and how far to step. These controllers spit out signals at high frequencies that energize certain winding pairs at just the right time to move the rotor with high precision and accuracy. The control software is very often very complicated because it has to take into account several factors like friction, inertia, torque, hysterisis – or left over magnetism - and the natural resonance of the system.

The number of windings in the stator and the number of teeth in the rotor determine the resolution of the steps. Suffice it to say that the more windings and the more teeth, the smaller the size of each step. And small steps are definitely a good thing when you want smooth and accurate movement and positioning, as in the case with beam positioning and indexable gobos. But

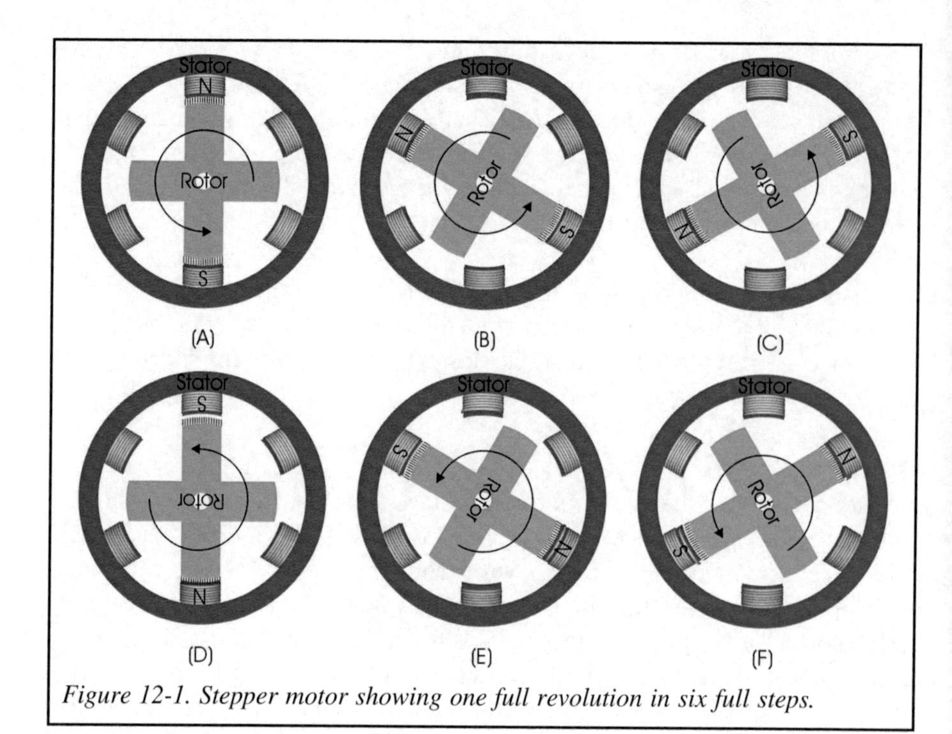

Figure 12-1. Stepper motor showing one full revolution in six full steps.

even the highest resolution stepper motor might have a maximum of 500 steps, which only yields a resolution of 0.72º. At fifty feet, one step would move 7.5" (19 cm), which would look very jagged and would make it very difficult to accurately pinpoint a target. Most moving lights boast of resolutions up to 0.3°.

The one thing that always intrigued me about stepper motors was how an open loop system – a system with no feedback – with four wires could rotate so smoothly and accurately position the shaft at any angle. I remember asking firmware engineers about exactly how many steps they were dealing with concerning the pan and tilt motors and it seemed that they would always invent a number.

"Uh, I think it's over a scadillion."

A scadillion? What the heck is a scadillion?

At the end of the 1980's and the early part of the 1990's it was not uncommon to find internal parts from various stepper motor – rotors, stators, leads, etc. – sprawled all over my desk. And there I would be counting teeth on the rotors trying to figure out what the heck a scadillion was. I never did find out.

What I did find was that the magic of fractional degree steps in a stepper motor is microstepping. Microstepping allows a stepper motor to stop and hold a position anywhere between a full and a half step position. We have already illustrated how a stepper motor moves in full steps by energizing a set of coils or windings on the stator, which in turn attract and move a magnet on the rotor. The size (or angle) of a full step can be calculated by subtracting the angle between coils from the angle between the magnets on the rotor.

$$\angle(\text{full step}) = \angle(\text{between rotor teeth}) - \angle(\text{between stator coils})$$

For example, a stepper with 96 coils and 64 rotor teeth has a 1.875° full step.

$$(360^\circ \text{ ¸ } 64) - (360^\circ \text{ ¸ } 96) = 1.875^\circ$$

The stepper takes a full step in the clockwise direction each time an adjacent coil is energized in the counter-clockwise direction.

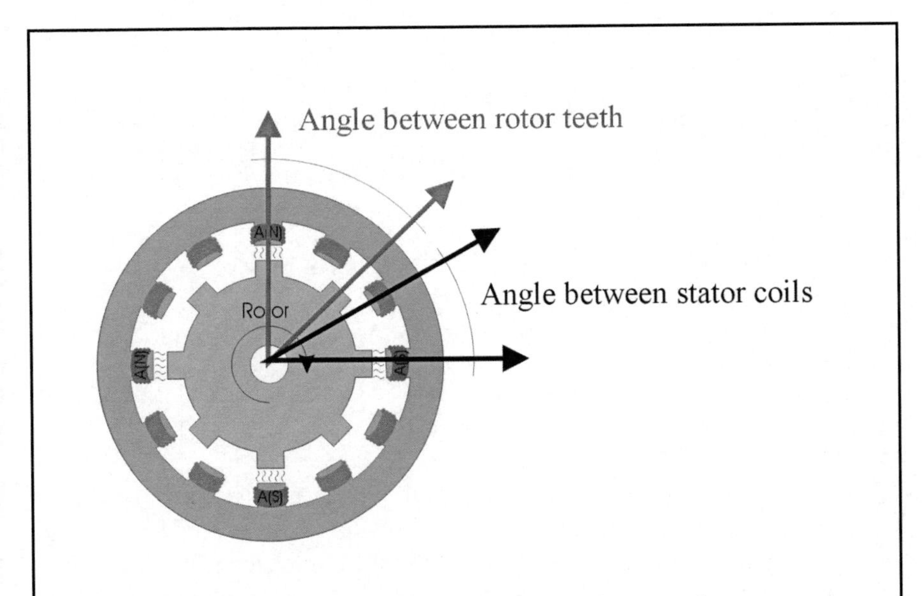

Figure 12-2. *The step size is a function of the angle between the rotor teeth and the angle between the stator coils.*

One Even Smaller Step

But a full step is a giant step in terms of pan and tilt. If you want to move the rotor a half step you can energize two adjacent coils simultaneously and they will produce a magnetic field that aligns the rotor teeth between the two coils, and a half step away from the single coil. Figure 12-3 below shows three steps in the sequence moving in half-step increments. In frame A., the four coils at the 12, 3, 6, and 9 o'clock position are energized, moving the rotor to align itself at the 90° position. Next, in frame B., two coils adjacent to each other and just to the counter-clockwise position from the last coil are energized. That moves and holds the rotor a half step clockwise. In frame C., one of the two coils is de-energized, again moving the rotor another half step clockwise. This sequence repeats itself until the rotor has rotated 180°. Then the sequence repeats again, only this time the polarity of the windings is reversed.

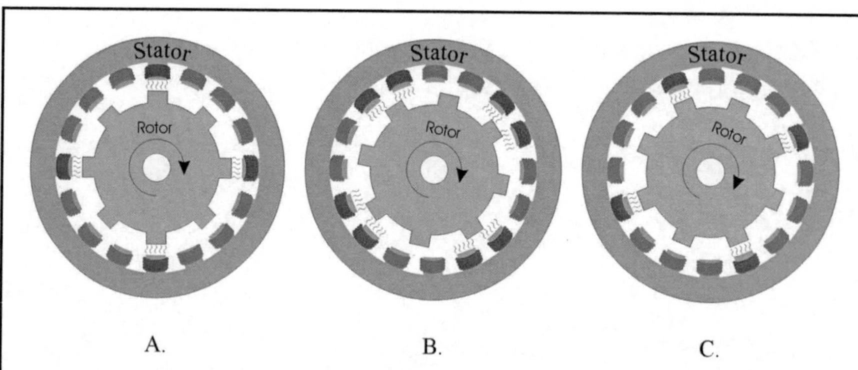

Figure 12-3. Stepper motor moving in half-step increments. A. Stator coil #1 is energized moving the rotor to the 90° position. B. Stator coils 2 and 3 are energized moving the rotor 11.5° clockwise from the previous position. C. Stator coil #2 is energized moving the rotor an additional 11.5° clockwise.

Stepping into the Microcosm

A full step is generally too large to move a light with any degree of accuracy or smoothness to be acceptable. Even if a full step was as small as 1° that would translate to about one foot (0.3 meters) of movement at a 57' (17.4 meters) projection distance. That would make for terrible jaggies on a slow diagonal fade. If you moved the focus point diagonally at a very slow speed you would see a one-foot (0.3 meters) horizontal movement followed by a one-foot vertical movement in a stair step fashion. Even half steps would not suffice. But how is microstepping accomplished?

By continuously varying the current in the stator coils (rather than simply turning them on and off), you can move or hold the rotor in microsteps as small as you wish. The trick is to control the current so that the holding torque in the two windings is equal to the single winding holding torque and the rotor will move smoothly through the rotation. Instead of using a square wave control signal, the ideal control signal is a combination of sine and cosine waves. One set of stator coils is controlled by a sine wave while another set is controlled by a cosine wave. They are exactly the same waveform only 90° out of phase with respect to each other. Consequently, this solution is often called sine-cosine microstepping.

Sine-cosine microstepping is common in certain types of stepper motors

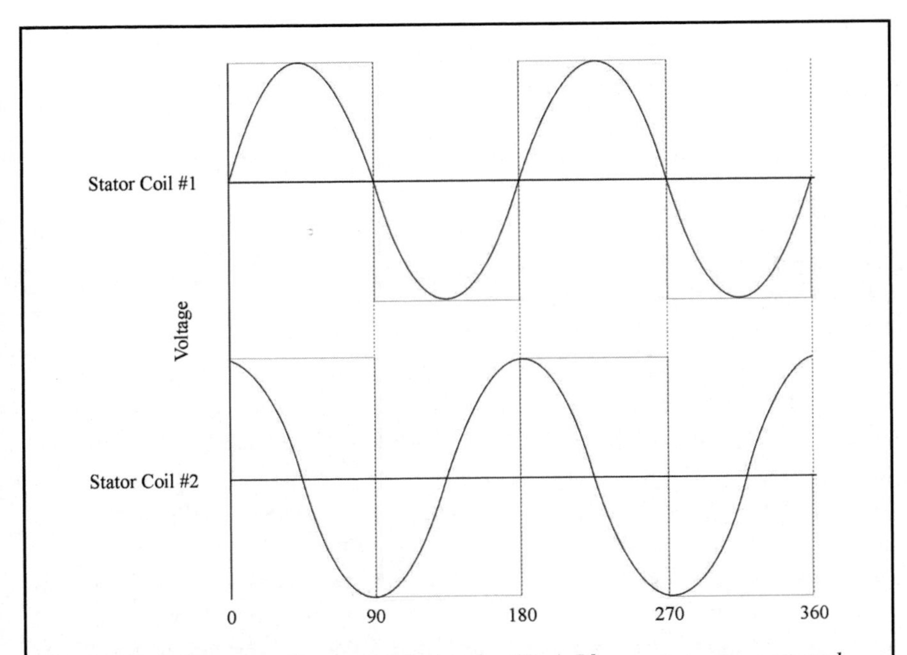

Figure 12-4. Stepper motor control signals. (Top) Blue square wave control signal moves stepper motor in full steps. Red sine wave varies position and torque continuously. (Bottom) Red cosine wave applies continuous torque to the second stator coil so that the sum of the torque in the first and second stator coils is constant.

such as two-winding variable reluctance or permanent magnet motors.

The other half of the equation is the electronic magic that converts the digital microprocessor information to an analog signal to which the motor can relate. The microprocessor generates a digital control signal which must then be converted to analog control information by a digital to analog converter chip (D/A chip). The resolution of the circuitry has a lot to do with how smoothly and accurately the stepper motor can move. Lower resolution circuits tend to produce stair-stepping beam movements in moving lights and contribute to positional inaccuracies. Higher resolution circuitry reduces but cannot eliminate the problem entirely.

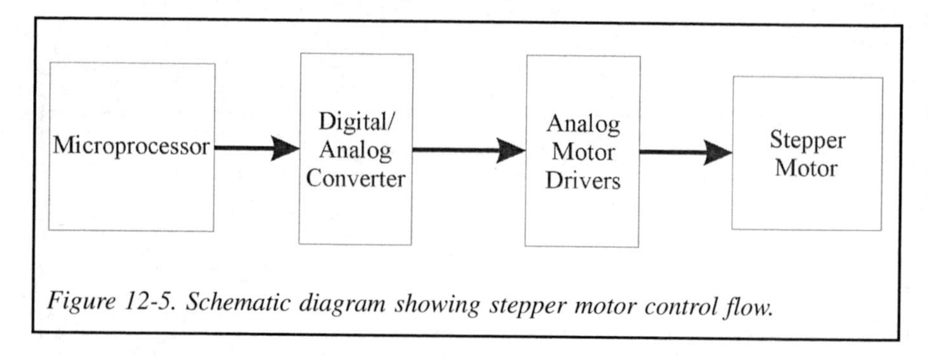

Figure 12-5. Schematic diagram showing stepper motor control flow.

Three Phase Stepper Motors

The new marketing buzz in moving lights is three-phase stepper motors. You'll see it on all the literature and specs for the new larger lights such as the Martin Mac 2000 and the High End Systems x.Spot. Three phase motors have three pairs of leads in parallel with all of the stator windings. All or all but one of the pairs is energized at every point in the control cycle, which provides for more even torque throughout the rotation cycle. It also provides for more torque for starting and stopping larger objects quicker.

Microstepping is a way of extending the performance of a stepper motor. It allows it to stop in virtually any position between a full and half step, and it can hold that position indefinitely. It makes for smoother movement, especially at slow speeds, and it reduces motor noise at intermediate speeds.

There is a lot more to stepper motors and stepper motor control than can fit in this book. If you're interest is piqued an excellent source of good information can be found at http://www.cs.uiowa.edu/~jones/step/index.html. Bring your math skills!

13 SWITCHING TO ENERGY EFFICIENT POWER SUPPLIES

"Any sufficiently advanced technology is indistinguishable from magic."
– Arthur C. Clarke

Over a hundred years ago the Niagara Falls Power Company wanted to harness the power of Niagara Falls and deliver it twenty-two miles to Buffalo, New York. They wanted to use the energy to drive the machines that fuel industry. It didn't matter to them if the energy was transferred in the form of mechanical energy, electrical energy, or otherwise. At the time, the idea was perplexing, perhaps considered insanely so, by some. Undaunted, the commission assigned to the task weighed their options between several alternatives, including alternating and direct current transmission. As is usually the case when more than one person is involved, there were several different opinions. Some people thought DC transmission the only practical method, while one or two others had a vision to use AC transmission. The main proponent of DC transmission was the well-known inventor Thomas Edison. His former employee, Nikoli Tesla almost single handedly paved the way for the technology for the practical application of AC transmission. He patented many of the developments that made it a household phenomenon.

The main problem with DC transmission is that there is no easy way to convert the voltage from one level to another. If you transmit power at a very high voltage, then it would be difficult to use once it was delivered. Have you ever tried to use a 47,000 VDC toaster? Trust me, you don't want to. On the other hand, if the voltage isn't high enough, then the current would have to be very large, which requires more copper, bigger transmission towers and fuses, ad infinitum. Besides heavy equipment costs, higher current results in bigger losses due to resistive heat dissipation. It's just plain inefficient.

AC transmission has the distinct advantage that a transformer can be used to change the voltage to level required for the job. You need to zap a few gigawatts over to Buffalo? No problem. Just use a transformer to convert it to 10K VAC and shuffle it off to Buffalo. You need some power for your toaster?

No problem. Just transform it back down to 115 VAC.

At the time, Edison had a lot invested in DC equipment – money, his business, and perhaps his pride. Meanwhile, George Westinghouse bought the patent rights to Tesla's induction motor – a key component in the so-called War of the Currents – and began to lobby in favor of AC transmission and distribution. Several factors turned the tide in favor of – you guessed it – AC transmission, not the least of which was the sharp increase in the cost of copper.

Today, a sharp increase in cost of power transmission and distribution on the West Coast in the U.S. might be a harbinger of things to come. The rolling blackouts in California are symptomatic of deregulation of electricity in that state. But hold on to your candles because more fun is on the way. The problem in California may or may not be short term. But the rising population, increasing modernization, and mass consumption all point towards one thing – increase demand for a finite resource called electricity. You don't have to be John Kenneth Galbraith to know that's a recipe for higher prices.

At the turn of the twentieth century, the so-called War of Currents ended with the widespread acceptance of AC power distribution. Today, in the entertainment lighting industry, manufacturers are fighting a war against gravity, volume, lamp mortality, flicker and energy consumption. Everyone wants lights to be smaller, lighter, brighter, better, and cheaper. Switching power supplies are helping them win the battle.

A switching power supply is a solid-state circuit that provides a constant voltage and just the right amount of power to handle a specific job. It can take the place of a magnetic power supply that operates any arc lamp, or any other load for that matter. They are smaller and lighter than a magnetic power supply, mainly because they don't use a ballast or choke.

A ballast is a coil of wire typically wound around an iron core. Its job is to resist any change in the flow of current, thus it is sometimes referred to as a "choke." As current flows in any conductor, it generates a magnetic field around it. When the conductor is wound around a cylinder into the shape of a coil, the magnetic field is reinforced and amplified. The magnetic field, in turn, generates a voltage in direct opposition to any change in current. If the current is increasing, the magnetic field, and in turn the voltage, increasingly opposes the current. If the current is decreasing, the magnetic field decreases and keeps the current from dropping too quickly.

A ballast is an integral part of a magnetic power supply circuit. It protects

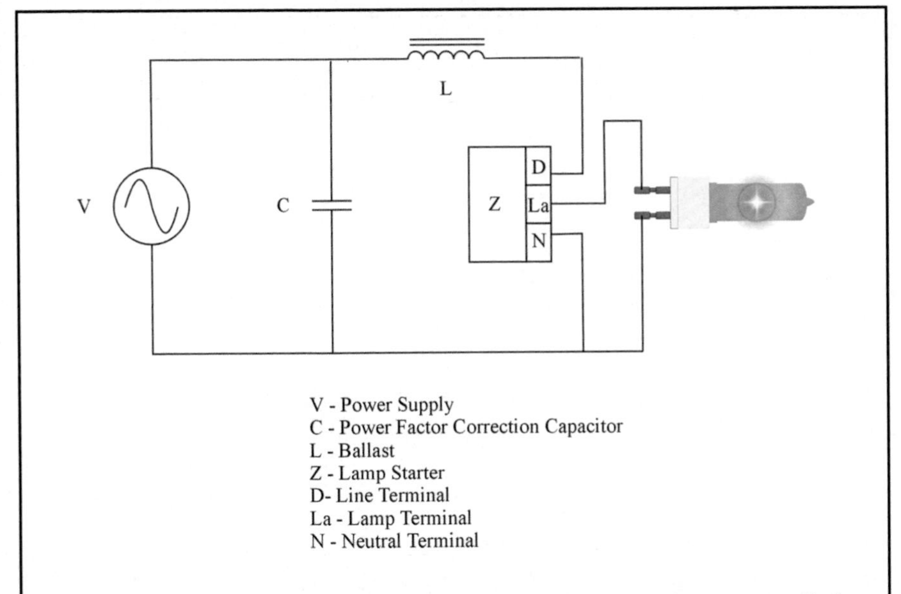

V - Power Supply
C - Power Factor Correction Capacitor
L - Ballast
Z - Lamp Starter
D- Line Terminal
La - Lamp Terminal
N - Neutral Terminal

Figure 13-1. *A magnetic power supply circuit. The input voltage is supplied by connecting to the power grid. The ballast, L, limits the current to the lamp. The lamp starter, Z, provides the high starting voltage necessary to begin the arcing process. The power factor correction capacitor, C, helps offset the inductance of the load and bring the voltage and current in phase with each other.*

the lamp by limiting the amount of current flowing through it. Without the ballast, the current would flow unimpeded and destroy the lamp. The amount of current that does flow through the lamp circuit is relatively high and requires relatively large gauge wire. Unfortunately, that makes the ballast very big and very heavy. The higher the wattage of the lamp, the bigger and heavier the ballast. A typical ballast for a 575 Watt fixture might weigh five or ten pounds.

An electronic switching power supply doesn't rely on a lot of copper windings to control the flow of current. Instead, it uses solid-state components that regulate the current and the voltage. Solid-state components like SCR's and switching transistors are much smaller and lighter than iron and copper components. They provide current and voltage regulation by means of a digital feedback circuit and a current switch. The feedback circuit monitors

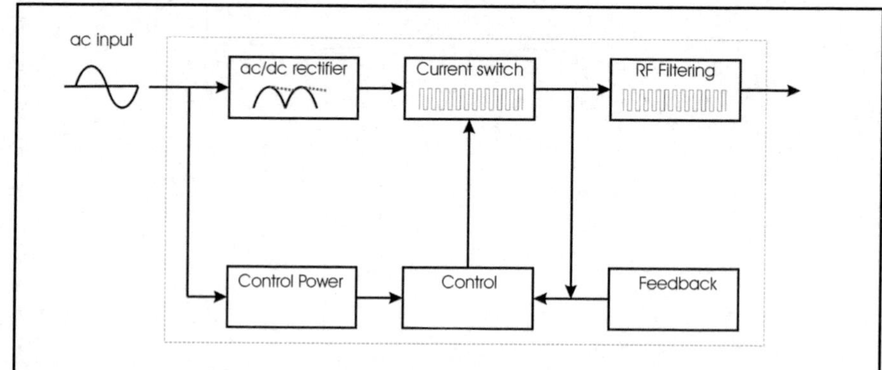

Figure 13-2. Block diagram of an electronic switching power supply. Electronic components take the place of the ballast in a magnetic power supply and increase efficiency.

the voltage and current, processes the information, and makes changes in the control of the devices. The current switch regulates how much current is allowed to pass to the load. Because the voltage drop across these components is much smaller than the voltage drop across a ballast, they dissipate less heat and they run more efficiently. There are no I^2R losses from the ballast because there is no ballast. Almost all of the power is transferred to the load.

A typical switching power supply block diagram is shown in the illustration above. It starts with a full-wave rectifier that converts the AC input to DC. The DC is fed into a very fast current switch, which is modulated, or turned on and off very fast, by a control circuit. The output of the switch is fed back and monitored by the controller circuit.

The controller is an integrated circuit chip that outputs a pulse-width-modulated signal. It also has error amplification that allows it to follow the output of the power supply and regulate it very closely.

There are many benefits that come with an electronic switching power supply:

- Efficiency - This type of power supply is very efficient because the power handling device, typically a MOSFET, has a relatively low voltage drop across the junction.
- Size and weight - It's lightweight because there is no ballast and relatively little copper. It's also smaller because the components are smaller.

- Flicker-free - It doesn't cause the lamp to flicker like a magnetic ballast power supply because the switching frequency is higher than that of a camera shutter. Several cycles will pass before the shutter of a camera opens and closes.
- Longer lamp life - It's easier on the lamp because the feedback and control circuit helps prevent overvoltage and overcurrent situations. It also controls how quickly the current rushes into the circuit. Consequently, the lamp will normally last longer.
- Auto-voltage sensing - An electronic switching power supply can be built to work over a wide range of input voltage. In some cases they have auto-voltage sensing that allows it to work on any power grid anywhere in the world.

But in lamp circuits, as in life, there are always trade-offs. All of these benefits come with a price. Literally. And that price is usually considerably higher than with a magnetic power supply. An electronic switching power supply can cost two or three times that of a magnetic power supply, possibly more. In the highly competitive entertainment lighting industry, many manufacturers first priority is meeting a low price point and they opt for the cheaper magnetic power supply.

Also, because they have fewer components, magnetic power supplies are inherently more reliable than electronic switching power supplies. With more components there is a statically higher probability of failure.

Electronic switching power supplies have been around for a long time and are very common in computers and other electronic devices. As more of them are manufactured, the economy of scale will make them more attractive in price and we will see them more commonly in entertainment lighting.

In the early part of the twentieth century, we were forced by economic conditions to develop alternating current power distribution. Now we are influenced by economic conditions to use magnetic power supplies. As the cost of generating electricity and building generating plants rises along with the demand, there will be a point where it becomes clear to the consumer that paying more for energy efficient power supplies is a good investment.

14 DICHROIC FILTERS AND GLASS GOBOS

"You've achieved success in your field when you don't know whether what you're doing is work or play."
– Warren Beatty

When I was a kid, besides having to walk uphill both ways to and from school through the driving rain (we lived in Corpus Christi, Texas – we didn't have snow), we also had to make our own circuit boards from scratch. I remember when I was fourteen and other kids were into really useful things like pet rocks and mood rings I saved up my cash and went shopping at the local Radio Shack. At that time, there were two places where they knew me by reputation – Radio Shack and Coastal Music, the local music store. They always loved to see me walk in the door because they knew that I would spend at least a buck or two after spending five hours looking, touching, playing and asking enough questions to rattle Mother Teresa. But on this particular day I threw them off by walking right into the Radio Shack store, going straight to the printed circuit board-making kit, and buying it right off. Twenty-nine years later they're still wondering how that happened.

I took my circuit board making kit home and built an audio effects box for my electric guitar. I took the green fiberboard with the copper coating and marked the circuit traces with a pen that could have passed as a Sharpie, but it was really a photoresist pen. After the circuit was drawn in exquisite detail (okay, it was a very simple schematic) I followed the instructions and dipped the whole board into a chemical bath to set the photoresist. Then after it dried I again dipped the board in a different chemical that etched away the copper everywhere except where I had drawn the electronic traces. Voilà! Instant PC board!

I didn't realize it at the time, but making that circuit board taught me a lot. First of all, it taught me that you really shouldn't pour etching chemicals down the sink, especially when your dad is in the same country. And years later, it also gave me a lot of insight about how glass gobos are made.

Glass gobos are the aesthetic salvation of modern theatrical lighting projection. The little glass patterns took us from the Flintstones to the Jetsons in one episode. Projections that used to look like cave drawings made by a modern stone-age family are now intricately carved light sculptures with vibrant colors and shading. Glass gobos are the enabling technology that gave us high-resolution photorealistic projections as well as colorful abstract images. What used to be limited by the hardware is now limited only by the designer's imagination.

As recently as ten or fifteen years ago, most gobo patterns were made of steel or aluminum. Before the advent of moving lights, you simply dropped a pattern into the gate of a leako and it projected a single image in black and white. Or more correctly, in light and shadow. With a good quality instrument you could project a nice clean image with sharp contrast, and by adding a gel or dichroic filter you could make it one color plus black. The problem with metal gobos is that they restrict your design by forcing you to create bridges to isolated areas. For example, the center of a tunnel effect with a metal gobo pattern needs three bridges to hold the centerpiece in place.

Metal gobos also tend to warp, making it difficult for them to exhibit uniform focus from the center to the edge. Nor are they able to project gray scale or multi-colored patterns. It's also difficult to render fine detail with metal gobos.

Figure 14-1. Metal gobo on left shown with telltale bridges and single color glass gobo on right with floating tunnel.

In fact, the finer the lines and bridges, the faster they will warp and burn out. Depending on the design and application, metal gobos need to be replaced relatively quickly.

Glass gobos provide lighting designers with the best possible image projection, clarity of the image, and color palette. Like dichroic filters, they are a very important part of the overwhelming majority of lights shows in production today. Lighting designers are demanding more glass gobos in their lighting fixtures and manufacturers are responding. The number of glass gobo manufacturers around the planet is growing.

Dichroic Filters

Glass gobos begin their life as dichroic filters. When I first wrote about dichroic filters for *Show Technology* magazine in 1989, few people in the entertainment lighting industry had firsthand knowledge of the little glass wonders. Up to that point, most lighting instruments used gel filters. Today, with the proliferation of automated lighting, few in our industry have not had extensive experience with dichroic filters and their close relatives, the glass gobo. It's been quite a while since I've heard anyone refer to them as "dichronic filters" or "dichromatic filters."

Dichroic filters are made by depositing a thin-film coating on a glass substrate. A thin-film coating is a very fine layer – a couple of microns or a couple of thousandths of an inch thick – of a dielectric material. Typically, silicon dioxide (SiO_2) and titanium dioxide (TiO_2) are used for coatings. They are applied by the process of vapor deposition under a very high vacuum in a vacuum chamber. The substrates are typically barium borosilicate glass, which is similar to Pyrex®, about one millimeter thick. This glass can withstand very high temperatures without melting and it has a very low thermal expansion characteristic. That's important because it helps keep the coating from separating from the substrate as the light energy heats it up to an incredibly high temperature. The combination of SiO_2, TiO_2, and borosilicate glass produces a super hard, durable filter.

The process of manufacturing optical coatings is similar to that of manufacturing integrated circuits. It is done in a vacuum chamber where the substrates are placed on a carrier, called a planetary, at the top of the chamber. The planetary serves to facilitate the uniform distribution of the deposition by spinning the substrates and rotating the entire carriage. At the bottom of the chamber, an electron beam scans a crucible loaded with SiO_2 or TiO_2. The electron beam vaporizes the crystals and the vapor diffuses throughout the chamber. Some of the vapor is deposited onto the glass producing a fine layer of dielectric coating. The operator uses detectors to monitor the thickness of the deposit, and when a predetermined thickness is deposited, she stops the deposition and changes from one type of dielectric to the other. The process continues with alternating layers placed one on top of the other. Several of these layers make up the coating of a typical dichroic filter. It can range from as few as three or five layers to as many as 30 or 40 layers.

The principle behind the magic of color separating dichroic filters is refraction, or the process of bending light. Every substance has a characteristic index of refraction, which is an indicator of how fast light travels through it relative to a vacuum. If light travels very slowly through a particular medium compared to a vacuum, then it has a very high index of refraction. If it travels close to the same speed as in a vacuum, then it has a low index of refraction. When light passes through an interface of two materials with different indices of refraction, it "bends" or changes direction. Every wavelength, or color, bends to a different degree when it encounters a change in the index of refraction. For that reason, white light will scatter into its component colors when it passes through an interface of two different materials with different indices of refraction. The greater the difference, the more the light scatters. What's more, light will bend towards a line drawn perpendicular to surface of

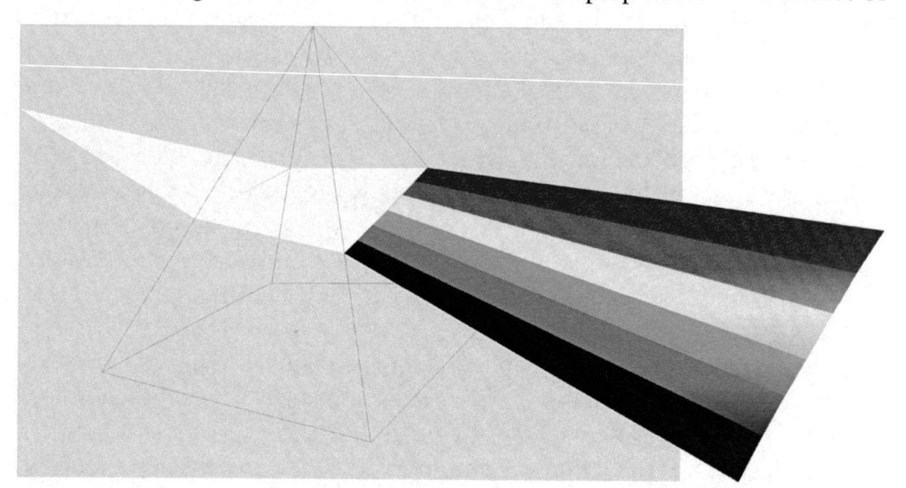

Figure 14-2. Example of white light refracting and scattering into component colors.

the boundary if it is traveling into a material with a higher index of refraction. If it is traveling into a material with a lower index of refraction, it will bend away from the perpendicular.

This is the principle that allows the dichroic filter designer to pick and choose which wavelengths to pass and which to reject. First the incident light is scattered as it passes from the air into the first layer of a dichroic filter because it has a higher index of refraction than air. That separates the colors of the spectrum. The next layer the light encounters is the second dielectric, say SiO_2. It has a lower index of refraction than the first layer, say TiO_2. Because of the way the layers alternate between a higher and lower index of refraction, the light is continually bent towards and away from the perpendicular line from the surface boundary of the dichroic filter. But keep in mind that some wavelengths bend more than others. So the wavelengths that bend the most end up redirected away from the dichroic filter back towards the light source. Others are directed at an angle away from the perpendicular and to the side of the filter. Still others follow a zigzag path through the filter. Those eventually end up passing straight through the filter. Those wavelengths that pass define the color of the filter. That's why dichroic filters produce a different color from the side than they do from the front of the filter. Alternatively, tilting a dichroic filter in the optical path of a light fixture produces a gradually changing color, much like Vari*Lite VL5. Just remember that if you use tilting dichroic filters in a fixture be prepared to pay Vari-Lite royalties because they own the patent for that.

Building a Better Mousetrap

Because of the inherent nature of dichroic filters, they have some very distinct advantages over colored gel. First and foremost, there is a very sharp separation between the colors the filter passes and the colors it rejects. If you look at a graph of the spectral distribution of a dichroic filter you will find that there is a very steep slope at the cut off point. Thus, the quality of the color produced by the dichroic filter is significantly more saturated and pure than that of a gel. There is little or no contamination of bordering colors. Dichroic colors have a very distinctive look. The only light I can think of with a more pure color is coherent light or laser light.

Secondly, there are very little losses due to absorption. The colors that are rejected by the filter are not absorbed or dissipated. They are redirected toward the light source or to the side of the filter. By contrast a gel absorbs unwanted colors and dissipates them in the form of heat. Energy can neither be created nor destroyed, but it can change forms. In the case of a gel it changes from light energy to heat energy. The heat has to be absorbed and dissipated by the polyester gel. The heat eventually destroys the gel, causing it to wrinkle, fade, and burn. How long a gel lasts depends on the color. How many times have you had to re-gel your Congo Blue gels? Once a week? Every other show perhaps? A dichroic filter, on the other hand, operates at approximately the same temperature independently of the color. Instead of absorbing energy it only bounces it away from the glass. That makes the

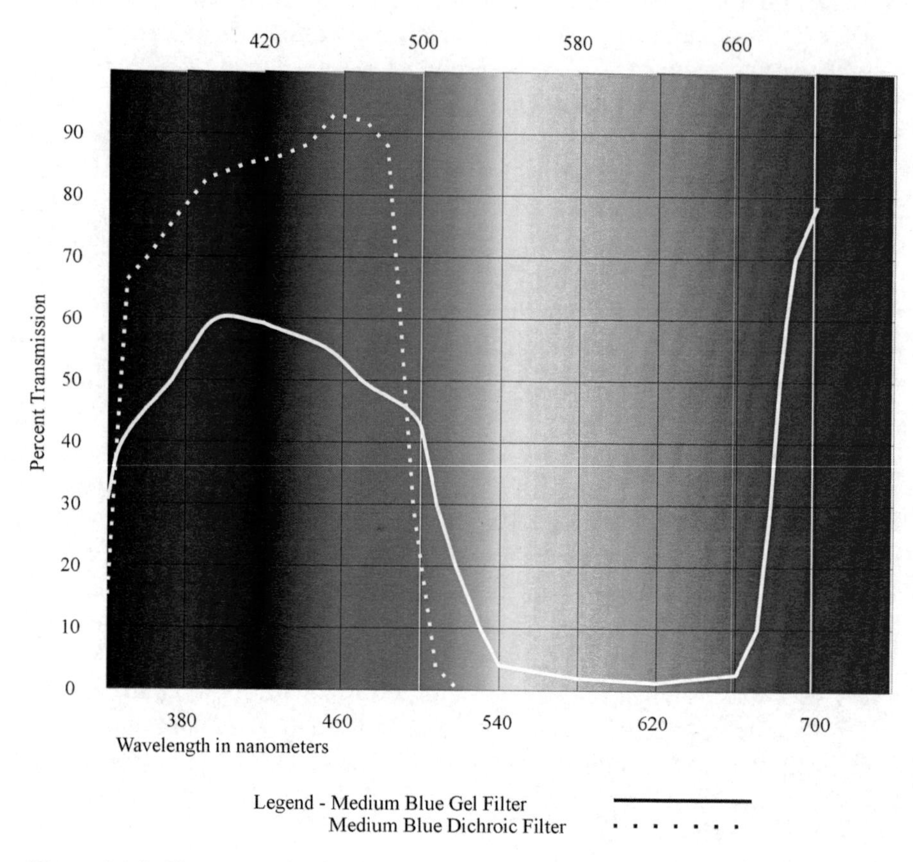

Figure 14-3. The spectral distribution curve for a gel filter and a dichroic filter. Notice that the slope of the cut off is much steeper for the dichroic filter. Also, the dichroic filter passes much more light than does the gel filter.

dichroic filter last for years, assuming the coating was applied correctly and adheres to the substrate. Otherwise the coating can peel off or eventually burn. Since there is little or no degradation of the thin-film coating, a dichroic filter will look exactly the same after years of use as it did the day it was manufactured.

Perhaps the most significant characteristic of the dichroic filter is that it is very efficient. Depending on the color, it can pass as much as 60% to 90% or more of the incident light in the desired wavelength. That's at least two or three times more efficient than a gel or colored glass. A fixture with a dichroic filter takes less energy to produce the same amount of color than one with a gel. Alternatively, a fixture with a dichroic filter produces more light than a fixture of equivalent light output with a gel. As long as the cost, generation and distribution of electricity is an issue, dichroic filters will become increasingly important in energy conservation.

Today, many people in the lighting industry understand the significance of using dichroic filters. They also understand that along with the benefits comes a price tag. In 1988, the company I was working for at the time, High

Figure 14-4. Graphical representation of how a dichroic filter works.

End Systems, started manufacturing dichroic filters. At that time, most optical coatings were being manufactured for scientific and military applications by companies like Balzers, Optical Coating Laboratories, Inc. (OCLI), and Bausch and Lomb. They were used in laser applications, infrared sensing devices, lamp reflectors and sunglasses. When High End built a thin-film lab and started manufacturing dichroic filters they dropped the price of filter by around a factor of 8. At the time we thought we could put a serious dent in the gel market and that every serious lighting system would be replete of gels and sporting all glass color media. It turns out that, at less than $10 in the U.S. for a 20" x 24" sheet of gel versus more than $1 per square inch for a dichroic filter, the economics are a hard sell. Indeed, with breakage and losses, it's hard to justify outfitting a PAR rig with dichroic filters, though it has been done.

Soon afterwards, dichroic manufacturers proliferated and dichroic filter stocks were on the rise. Manufacturers looked for ways to move inventory. The next logical step was to produce glass gobos from the dichroic filters.

Got Glass Gobos?

Glass gobos are nothing more than dichroic filters onto which an image has been etched. The etching process is the same, in principle, as that used to etch circuit boards. The substrate in glass gobos, of course, is not made of fiberboard and copper, but it is a finished dichroic filter. Or, in the case of a black and white or grayscale gobo, a first surface mirror. A first-surface mirror, like those used on moving mirror fixtures and as laser bounce mirrors, are manufactured exactly the same way as a dichroic filter with one exception. Instead of titanium dioxide and silicon dioxide, the glass is coated with aluminum and silicon dioxide.

The production of a custom made glass gobo starts with a computer file of the image to be produced. There are several computer graphics programs that can be used to create images. Two of the most popular are Adobe® Illustrator® and Adobe® PhotoShop®. Some manufacturers are producing glass gobos with 10,000 or 12,000 dpi resolution. It's important to start with good quality high-resolution graphics files. The images are only as good as the weakest link and the best manufacturing process in the world won't improve poor quality low-resolution images. Once the lighting designer or graphics illustrator has created an image file, it can be submitted to a manufacturer for the production of a glass gobo. The production personnel will import the file into their own graphics program and output the image to film. The film is then used as a photomask to etch an exact image on the coated glass using a photolithography process.

Photolithography

The first step in the photolithography process is to coat the filter with a polymer that is sensitive to ultraviolet light, called photoresist. The photoresist, once it has been exposed, protects the thin-film coating from the etching chemicals. The next step is to set or activate the photoresist with ultraviolet light, which strengthens the polymer. In this step the film is used to mask the UV light and activate only the portion of the photoresist that is to be protected from the etching chemicals. The unexposed portions form the image, as projected by the photomask, and will be etched away. Finally, filter is bathed in etching chemicals to complete the pattern. If the coated glass is a single color or a first surface mirror, then the gobo will be a single color gobo, or a black and white or grayscale gobo, respectively. For multi colored gobos, single color gobos can be stacked and banded to retain their orientation. Or they can be returned to the thin-film lab and photolithography lab for a second round of coating and etching.

The cost of glass gobos varies by manufacturer. Black and white and grayscale gobos are the least expensive, and multi-colored gobos are the most expensive. The more colors in the gobo the more expensive they are. Custom gobos are also more expensive than stock patterns. For custom gobos there is normally a one-time set up charge, or tooling charge, which covers the cost of producing the photomask film. Once that is paid for each additional gobo is relatively inexpensive, depending on the number of colors involved. You can pay anywhere from around $100 in the U.S. for a stock, black and white gobo, to over $1000 for a custom multi-colored gobo.

The manufacturers of the fixtures that are projecting these images have increasingly improved the optics to the point where the resolution of the images has become very important. Many fixtures now have achromatic lenses, improved lamp sources with better color balance, and short arc lamps that allow for much smaller optics. These improvements have rendered lower resolution gobos more unacceptable because you can see the steps of resolution better.

By the same token, manufacturers of glass gobos have risen to the challenge. They are producing amazingly creative and beautiful multicolored and photo realistic gobos with very high resolution. Companies such as Rosco (www.rosco.com) and Apollo Design Technology (www.internetapollo.com) have increased resolution of some of their products to 10,000 to 12,000 dots per inch while devising new ways to marry dichroic filters, textured glass, and both photographic and abstract images.

Photolithography is one way to manufacture glass gobos. Vari-Lite (www.vari-lite.com) does it by oblating, or cutting away, the dichroic coating with a laser beam, thus producing a tiny dot through which light can pass. The remainder of the coating produces the dark portion of the image.

I think I would have enjoyed laser oblation as a kid, but I never had the opportunity. My cousin, who was a couple of years older than me, built his first ruby laser at age fourteen. If only he had built a Carbon Dioxide or a YAG laser we could have oblated lots of stuff.

15 REFLECTOR GEOMETRY

"We all walk in the dark, and each of us must learn to turn on his or her own light."
– Earl Nightingale

My earliest experience with automated lights was sometime around the Mesozoic era when dinosaurs roamed the earth. To be more precise, it was during the last millennium, towards the end of the last century, around the middle part of the ninth decade. Let's just call it 1986. There were approximately two 'prehistoric' moving lights that you could buy at the time – the Coemar Robot and the Clay Paky Golden Scan. These machines were made in Italy but they were known to roam all parts of the earth. Simple though they were, they were at least effective. They had similar features – color wheel, gobo wheel, shutter, pan and tilt – but they were as different as brontosaurus and t-rex. The Robot creature had an HTI 250 lamp, which was later evolved into an MSR 400, while the Golden Scan used 575 watt or 1200 watt HMI lamps. The Robots used servo motors while the Golden Scan had more highly evolved stepper motors. The Robot was a short creature with black markings while the Golden Scans were long and slender with a silver finish. But the biggest difference of all was the beam coming out of the fixtures. The beam profile was very different between the two. The Robot output was bright and had a hot spot in the center. The Golden Scan appeared to have a higher color temperature, which made the beam appear blue-ish, and the field was very flat. It had a better center-to-edge focus.

The difference between these two early automated light machines represents two distinct design approaches in building light fixtures. The Robot used an elliptical reflector design and the Golden Scan used a spherical reflector design. Those types of reflectors are still the dominant designs in automated lighting fixtures on the market today. Clay Paky still uses spherical reflectors, as do SGM, Robert Juliat, and others. Elliptical reflectors are more common in fixtures built by Coemar, High End Systems, Martin, and Vari-Lite.

There are at least three types of reflectors used in entertainment lighting – spherical, elliptical, and parabolic reflectors. Parabolic reflectors are most commonly used in PAR (*parabolic* aluminized reflector) lamps. But the vast majority of optical systems in entertainment lighting use either elliptical or spherical reflectors.

Tennis Anyone?

If you took a tennis ball and sliced off about a third of it you would have the geometry of a spherical reflector. It wouldn't do much good for your tennis game, nor would it reflect much light, but it does give you an idea of how a spherical reflector works. If there was a light source at the center of what used to be the tennis ball, and if the inside surface were coated with reflective material, then all of the reflected light would be directed right back to the source. As you move the light source closer to the surface of the reflector the reflected light diverges and the focal point moves away from the reflector.

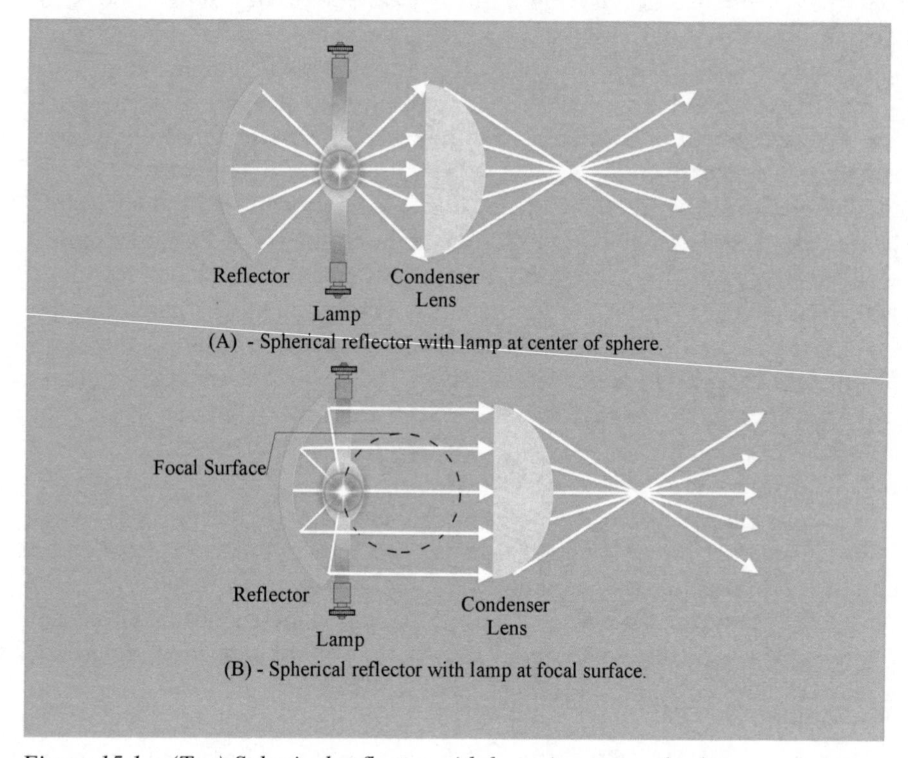

Figure 15.1 – (Top) Spherical reflector with lamp in center of sphere. (Bottom) Spherical reflector with lamp on focal surface.

When the light source is halfway between the center of the ball and the inside surface of the ball, then it would be on the focal surface of the reflector. At that point, the reflected light would be redirected in parallel rays away from the reflector.

Lights with spherical reflectors are often teamed up with a condenser lens, whose job it is to collect the reflected light and focus it on the gobo plane.

Read My Ellipse

If you took a football and sliced off about a third of it, you would have something that sorta kinda resembles the geometry of an elliptical reflector. I know that's not very scientific, but I'm trying to paint a picture in your mind. Work with me! Okay, to be more exact, you could take an ellipse and rotate it about its axis to create an ellipsoid. Then if you cut off about a third of it you would have the geometry of an elliptical reflector. If you remember the ellipse from your geometry class then you know that an ellipse has two foci. If you place a light source at one focus of an elliptical reflector, then the reflected light will converge on the other focus.

Elliptical reflectors engulf more of the light source than do spherical reflectors. As a result, they reflect more light produced by the source and they're more efficient than spherical reflectors. But a lot of the light is reflected towards the center of the beam. Fixtures with elliptical reflectors tend to be brighter at the center of the beam, but have more drop-off toward the edge of the beam.

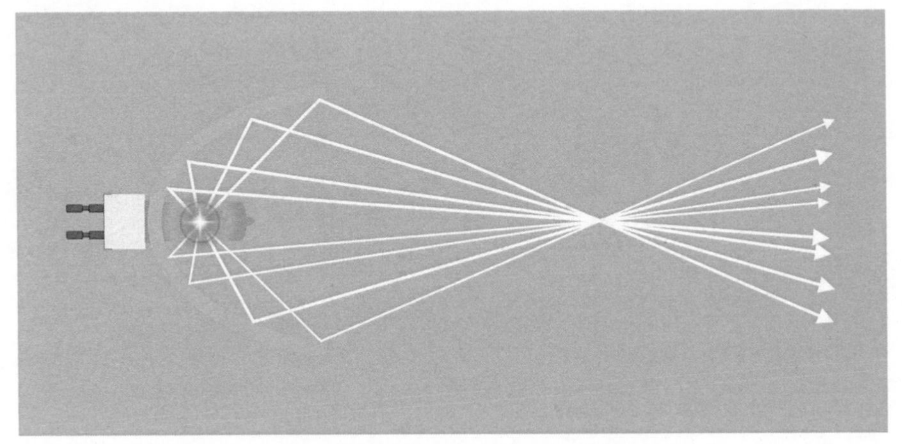

Figure 15.2 - Elliptical reflector with lamp at focus of ellipse.

Spherical reflectors, on the other hand, produce a more uniform beam with less of a hot spot in the center. The uniformity of the beam with a spherical reflector helps the fixture produce a better center-to-edge focus and a sharp, crisp focus. They tend to be better at projecting sharp, crisp images that are focused in the entire field.

The choice of reflector geometry is not the only factor affecting the uniformity of the beam, efficiency of the fixture, and the center-to-edge focus. The reflector material, whether it's aluminum or coated glass, has a big influence on the efficiency and cost of the fixture. A dichroic reflector is highly efficient, if a bit more expensive, and it can be tuned to reflect only visible light and not UV or IR. It can heavily influence the color temperature of the light produced by the fixture. The quality of other optics elements also affects the characteristics of the fixture.

The lighting manufacturer's first design consideration is the reflector geometry. That choice heavily influences the characteristics of the light output. They can start with a really bright beam or with really good focus and beam uniformity. What happens from there is what separates the carnivores from the herbivores.

16 TECHNOLOGY CRYSTAL BALL

"The best way to predict the future is to invent it."
- Alan Kay, Vice President, Research & Development and Disney Fellow, Walt Disney Imagineering.

I, the all-seeing, all-knowing Swami Candela of the Devine Light of the Short Arc, predict that by the year 2011, there will be an automated lighting instrument on the market that will revolutionize the industry. But then, it's nearly impossible to predict the future with great accuracy. There are paid professionals who make a darn good living as prognosticators. Some are better than others are, but most are very well paid. And most of them all do a miserable job of accurately predicting the future. Two that come to mind are stock market analysts and meteorologists. If I did my job with as much inaccuracy as these two groups I dare say I would be in the unemployment line before I could say "devitrification." Still, like moths drawn to a flame, we have an innate desire to ponder the future and predict what it has in store.

Howard Rhengold is a writer who said, "You can't really guess where … technology is going unless you understand where it came from." I agree. It is easier to see where we're going if we can identify trends and see where we've been. In the realm of automated lighting, we have a relatively short history, about fifteen years, of data with which to identify trends. Fortunately for us, the data is very clear. Since the first automated lights were built around 1972, they have all gotten smaller, lighter, brighter, more affordable and much better.

If my research is accurate, the first automated moving light was called the Cyclops. It was designed and built by lighting designer Stefan Graf and then-electrician Jim Fackert, who were working with Grand Funk Railroad in the very early 1970's. Jim was playing around with servomotors and he came up with the idea to put a moving mirror on a followspot to automate it. When he mentioned it, Stefan thought Jim was one volt short of a kilowatt. But they were successful in marrying a followspot body with a moving mirror and the Cyclops was born in 1972. It was a basic version of automated lighting by today's standards. It had pan and tilt, zoom, an iris, a shutter for strobing, a mechanical dowser for dimming, and a six color solenoid-actuated boomerang for color change. And it worked like a charm. It toured with Grand Funk Railroad from 1972 until 1978. When it came off the road with GFR, it toured with various bands including War, Neil Diamond, Blue Oyster Cult, Johnny Winter, Edgar Winter, and REO Speedwagon. If you saw any of these shows in the '70's, then perhaps you witnessed the birth of an industry. Two people who did were Rusty Brutsché and Jim Bornhorst. They went on to become CEO and head of R&D for Vari-Lite.

The Cyclops was huge by today's standards – four feet long, a foot and a half wide, and it weighed eighty pounds – without the 150-pound ballast. All that and it was all of 500 watts.

About ten years later, Vari-Lite was building the VL1 and Cameleon was building the Telescan Mark I. The Telescan Mark I was a 1200-watt moving mirror fixture that was slightly over three feet long and weighed just over 100 pounds. Still very large and heavy by today's standards, it was clearly a step in the right direction. Not only was it smaller and lighter than the Cyclops was, it was also extremely bright.

The VL1 was much smaller and weighed about 48 pounds and in this first incarnation of the VL series used a Mark 350 lamp. It had six control channels including pan, tilt, dimming, color hue, color saturation, and gobo selection.

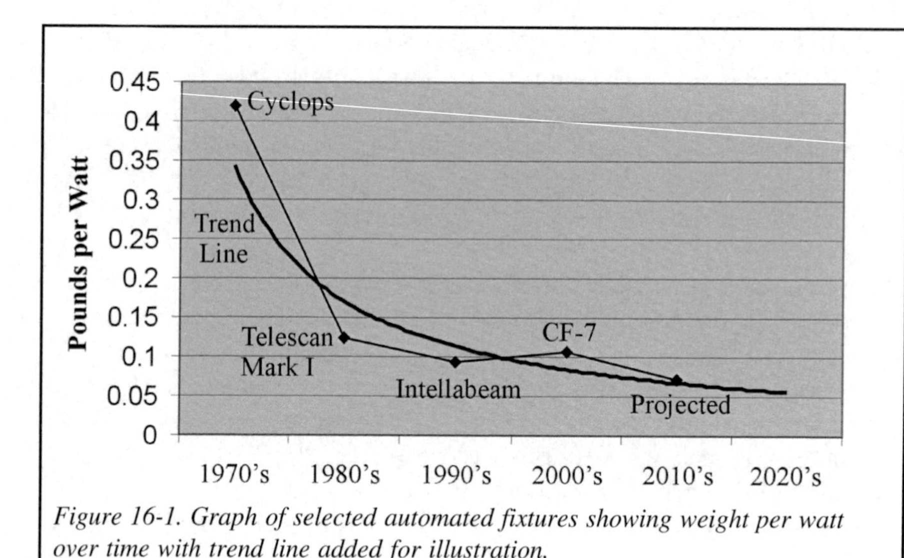

Figure 16-1. Graph of selected automated fixtures showing weight per watt over time with trend line added for illustration.

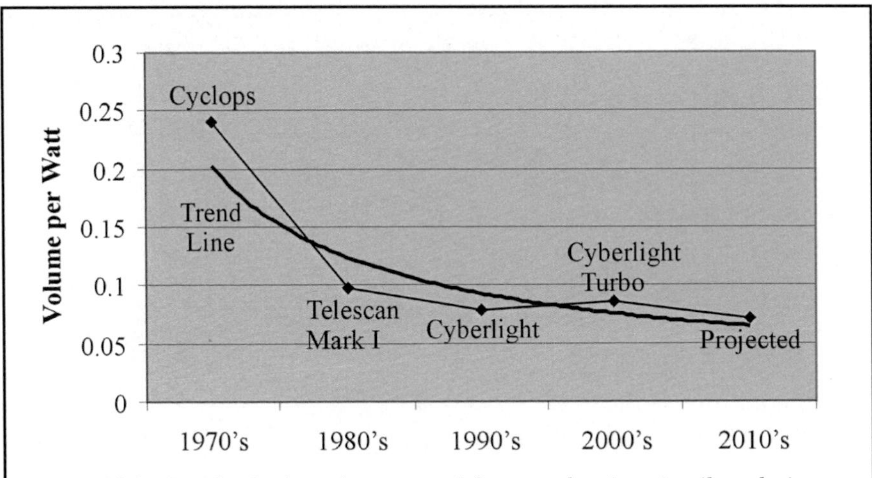

Figure 16-2. Graph of selected automated fixtures showing size (length times girth) per watt over time with trend line added in for illustration.

By 1991, High End Systems was building and selling the Intellabeam and had begun working on the Cyberlight. When the Cyberlight started shipping in the middle of the decade, it was a 1200-watt fixture that produced 8000 lumens, or almost seven lumens per watt. A few years later, they retrofitted the instrument with a Philips MSR 1200 short arc lamp and increased the light output over fifty percent. The Cyberlight Turbo produces more than ten lumens per watt. This improvement vividly illustrates where lamp and optical technology is heading. Lamp technology will continue to evolve and become more efficient and the entertainment lighting industry will be the beneficiary. Small, incremental improvements in lamps combined with increased efficiency in optics and power supplies are clearly in our future.

All the while, as automated lighting has become smaller, lighter, and brighter, the cost per lumen has come down while the feature set has risen dramatically. In 1989, the Coemar Robot was one of the first automated fixtures to be sold on the open market. It had a list price in the U.S. of $4000 and produced about 4000 lumens. It had a basic feature set that included pan and tilt (about 180° by 90°), a four-position color wheel, and a four-position gobo wheel that doubled as the shutter. Today, there are a number of 250-watt moving yoke fixtures that produce close to 4000 lumens and cost less than $2500. And they do much more than the Robot did, including 540° pan by 270° tilt (with position

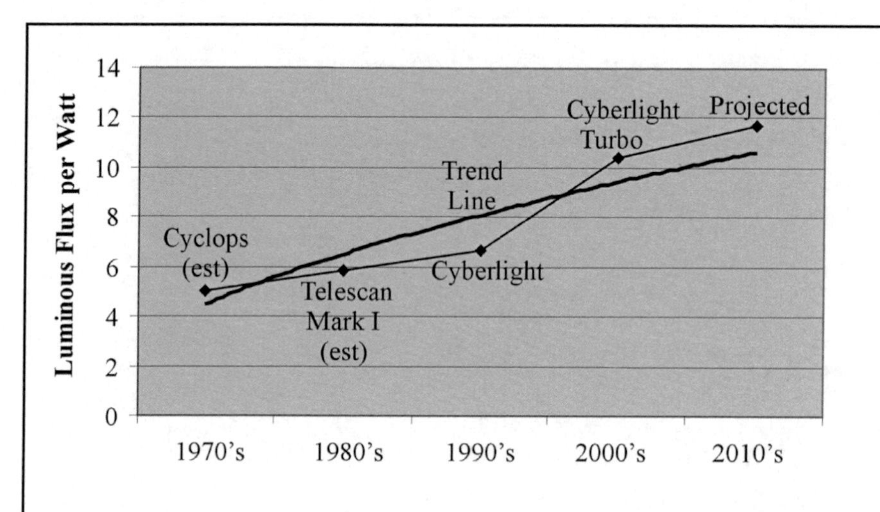

Figure 16-3. Graph of selected automated fixtures showing luminous flux per watt with trend line added for illustration.

encoding), rotating indexable dichroic glass gobos, remote focus, full dimming and rotating prisms. We went from Model A to the space shuttle in fifteen years.

How is it possible that we could some so far so fast? We have made advances in every aspect of luminaire construction and design. We have more efficient power supplies, improved lamps, better optics, better construction materials, and better design tools. Thanks in large part to the computer industry, we have the ability to build electronic switching power supplies that are much more efficient than they were a few years ago. That will continue to be a priority as our energy resources become more precious and our ability to meet our energy requirements becomes more strained. New designs such as resonant mode switching are just being introduced to our industry.

Lamp manufacturers will continue to make improvements in efficiency and performance. The 700-watt short arc fixtures (High End x.Spot, Coemar CF7, and more to come) have proven that we can get up the lumens per watt curve very quickly with short arc lamps. I believe that there will be great strides made in the area of longer lamp life. The entertainment lighting industry has been flirting with the architectural market, but until we can produce fixtures with 10,000 hours of lamp life or more, the architainment dream will always be like a long distance relationship. We'll spend a lot of time talking on the phone and a lot of lonely nights hoping for consummation of a deal. And speaking of dreams, I can only dream about the possibility of selective wavelength resonance, which would allow you to produce any color light without the use of filters.

Our optical engineers are pushing the limits of reflector efficiency with high-order aspherical reflector design. And space-age plastics and resins are enabling us to build stronger, lighter housings and internal parts. At the same time, we are able to bring products to market faster with rapid prototyping techniques such as stereolithography (SLA). SLA is a rapid prototyping technology that can produce solid parts very quickly using only a 3-D CAD file. The process uses a UV laser to scan and cure an epoxy photopolymer by sampling thin slices of the 3-D CAD drawing, turning it into a solid. What used to take weeks to produce prototypes now takes hours. That is extremely important in speeding new products to market. And new products are the life-giving blood of an automated fixture manufacturer.

We have started to reach the point of diminishing returns as the improvements are coming in smaller increments. But we still have a long way to go before we reach the end of the road on which we currently travel. The next big revolution in electronics will happen when we go from microelectronics to

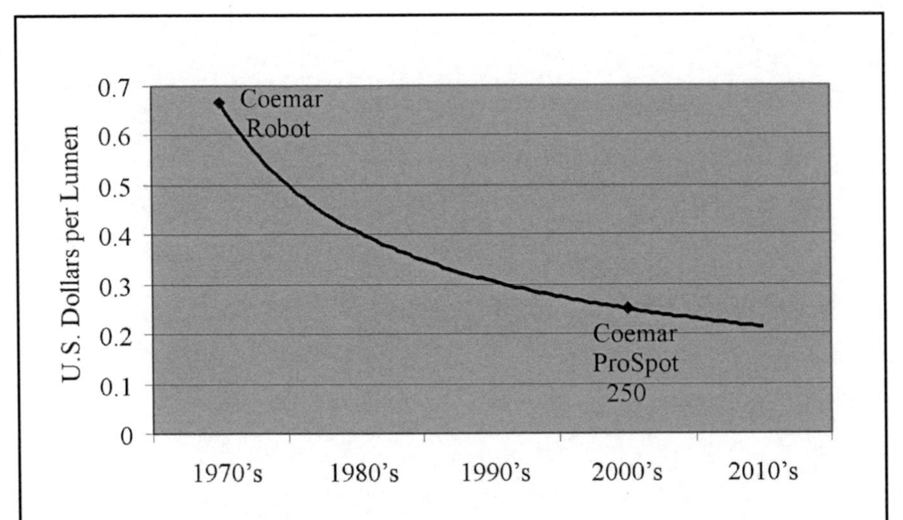

Figure 16-4. Graph of selected automated fixtures showing cost in U.S. dollars per lumen with trend line added for illustration.

nanoelectronics. Instead of using the photolithography process to build integrated circuits we will program molecules to assemble themselves into integrated circuits. These circuits will be much smaller and faster than anything we know. They will have the ability to repair themselves and they will be used for a wide variety of applications including medicine, agriculture, and, yes, even automated lighting. When will this happen? The Swami thinks it will happen by the year 2011.

The truth is, we don't need a crystal ball to see the future of automated lighting; we need a rear view mirror. I believe the past is the prologue and the future is smaller, lighter, brighter, more affordable and all around better than any light we have yet to see. And if I'm wrong, hey, I could always go back to school and become a meteorologist or a stock analyst.

INDEX

ENTERTAINMENT TECHNOLOGY PRESS

FREE SUBSCRIPTION SERVICE

Keeping Up To Date with

Focus on Lighting Technology

Entertainment Technology Press titles are continually up-dated, and all changes and additions are listed in date order in the relevant dedicated area of the publisher's website. Simply go to the front page of www.etnow.com and click on the BOOKS button. From there you can locate the title and be connected through to the latest information and services related to the publication, including the tender specification examples in this book available for download.

Comments on this publication can be made via the editor at editor@etnow.com or direct to the author at: rcadena@austin.rr.com

Titles Published by Entertainment Technology Press

ABC of Theatre Jargon *Francis Reid* **£9.95**
This glossary of theatrical terminology explains the common words and phrases that are used in normal conversation between actors, directors, designers, technicians and managers.

Aluminium Structures in the Entertainment Industry *Peter Hind* **£24.95**
Aluminium Structures in the Entertainment Industry aims to educate the reader in all aspects of the design and safe usage of temporary and permanent aluminium structures specific to the entertainment industry – such as roof structures, PA towers, temporary staging, etc.

Basics - A Beginner's Guide to Stage Lighting *Peter Coleman* **£9.95**
This title does what it says: it introduces newcomers to the world of stage lighting. It will not teach the reader the art of lighting design, but will teach beginners much about the 'nuts and bolts' of stage lighting.

Basics - A Beginner's Guide to Stage Sound *Peter Coleman* **£9.95**
This title does what it says: it introduces newcomers to the world of stage sound. It will not teach the reader the art of sound design, but will teach beginners much about the 'nuts and bolts' of stage lighting.

A Comparative Study of Crowd Behaviour at Two Major Music Events *Chris Kemp, Iain Hill, Mick Upton* **£7.95**
A compilation of the findings of reports made at two major live music concerts, and in particular crowd behaviour, which is followed from ingress to egress.

The Exeter Theatre Fire *David Anderson* **£24.95**
This title is a fascinating insight into the events that led up to the disaster at the Theatre Royal, Exeter, on the night of September 5th 1887. The book details what went wrong, and the lessons that were learned from the event.

Health and Safety Aspects in the Live Music Industry *Chris Kemp, Iain Hill* **£30.00**
This title includes chapters on various safety aspects of live event production and is written by specialists in their particular areas of expertise.

Hearing the Light *Francis Reid* **£24.95**
This highly enjoyable memoir delves deeply into the theatricality of the industry. The author's almost fanatical interest in opera, his formative period as lighting designer at Glyndebourne and his experiences as a theatre administrator, writer and teacher make for a broad and unique background.

Focus on Lighting Technology *Richard Cadena* **£17.95**
This concise work unravels the mechanics behind modern performance lighting and appeals to designers and technicians alike. Packed with clear, easy-to-read diagrams, the book provides excellent explanations behind the technology of performance lighting.

An Introduction to Rigging in the Entertainment Industry *Chris Higgs* **£24.95**
This book is a practical guide to rigging techniques and practices and also thoroughly covers safety issues and discusses the implications of working within recommended guidelines and regulations.

Lighting for Roméo and Juliette *John Offord* **£26.95**
John Offord describes the making of the production from the lighting designer's viewpoint - taking the story through from the point where director Jürgen Flimm made his decision not

to use scenery or sets and simply employ the expertise of Patrick Woodroffe.

Lighting Systems for TV Studios *Nick Mobsby* **£35.00**
Lighting Systems for TV Studios is the first book written specifically on the subject and is set to become the 'standard' resource work for the sector as it covers all elements of system design – rigging, ventilation, electrical as well as the more obvious controls, dimmers and luminaires.

Lighting Techniques for Theatre-in-the-Round *Jackie Staines*, **£24.95**
Lighting Techniques for Theatre-in-the-Round is a unique reference source for those working on lighting design for theatre-in-the-round for the first time. It is the first title to be published specifically on the subject, it also provides some anecdotes and ideas for more challenging shows, and attempts to blow away some of the myths surrounding lighting in this format.

Lighting the Stage *Francis Reid* **£14.95**
Lighting the Stage discusses the human relationships involved in lighting design – both between people, and between these people and technology. The book is written from a highly personal viewpoint and its 'thinking aloud' approach is one that Francis Reid has used in his writings over the past 30 years.

Pages From Stages *Anthony Field* **£17.95**
Anthony Field explores the changing style of theatres including interior design, exterior design, ticket and seat prices, and levels of service, while questioning whether the theatre still exists as a place of entertainment for regular theatre-goers.

Practical Guide to Health and Safety in the Entertainment Industry
Marco van Beek **£14.95**
This book is designed to provide a practical approach to Health and Safety within the Live Entertainment and Event industry. It gives industry-pertinent examples, and seeks to break down the myths surrounding Health and Safety.

Production Management *Joe Aveline* **£17.95**
Joe Aveline's book is an in-depth guide to the role of the Production Manager, and includes real-life practical examples and 'Aveline's Fables' – anecdotes of his experiences with real messages behind them.

Rigging for Entertainment: Regulations and Practice *Chris Higgs* **£19.95**
Continuing where he left off with his highly successful *An Introduction to Rigging in the Entertainment Industry*, Chris Higgs' new book covers the regulations and use of equipment in greater detail.

Sixty Years of Light Work *Fred Bentham* **£26.95**
This title is an autobiography of one of the great names behind the development of modern stage lighting equipment and techniques.

Sound for the Stage *Patrick Finelli* **£24.95**
Patrick Finelli's thorough manual covering all aspects of live and recorded sound for performance is a complete training course for anyone interested in working in the field of stage sound, and is a must for any student of sound.

Stage Lighting for Theatre Designers *Nigel Morgan* **£17.95**
An updated second edition of this popular book for students of theatre design outlining all the techniques of stage lighting design.

Technical Marketing Techniques *David Brooks, Andy Collier, Steve Norman* **£24.95**
Technical Marketing is a novel concept, recently defined and elaborated by the authors of this book, with business-to-business companies competing in fast developing technical product sectors.

Theatre Engineering and Stage Machinery *Toshiro Ogawa* **£30.00**
Theatre Engineering and Stage Machinery is a unique reference work covering every aspect of theatrical machinery and stage technology in global terms.

Theatre Lighting in the Age of Gas *Terence Rees* **£24.95**
Entertainment Technology Press is delighted to be republishing this valuable historic work previously produced by the Society for Theatre Research in 1978. *Theatre Lighting in the Age of Gas* investigates the technological and artistic achievements of theatre lighting engineers from the 1700s to the late Victorian period.

Walt Disney Concert Hall *Patricia MacKay & Richard Pilbrow* **£28.95**
Spanning the 16-year history of the design and construction of the Walt Disney Concert Hall, this book provides a fresh and detailed, behind the scenes story of the design and technology from a variety of viewpoints. This is the first book to reveal the "process" of the design of a concert hall.

Model National Standard Conditions *ABTT/DSA/LGLA* **£20.00**
These *Model National Standard Conditions* covers operational matters and complement *The Technical Standards for Places of Entertainment*, which describes the physical requirements for building and maintaining entertainment premises.

Technical Standards for Places of Entertainment *ABTT/DSA* **£30.00**
Technical Standards for Places of Entertainment details the necessary physical standards required for entertainment venues.